GREAT B

Also available in Piccolo True Adventures

Aidan Chambers
HAUNTED HOUSES
MORE HAUNTED HOUSES
GREAT GHOSTS OF THE WORLD

Richard Garrett
HOAXES AND SWINDLES
TRUE TALES OF DETECTION
NARROW SQUEAKS!
GREAT SEA MYSTERIES

Frank Hatherley
BUSHRANGERS BOLD!

Carey Miller
AIRSHIPS AND BALLOONS
SUBMARINES!

Nicholas Monsarrat
THE BOYS' BOOK OF THE SEA

Eric Williams
GREAT AIR BATTLES

Piccolo True Adventures

GREAT BRITISH GHOSTS

AIDAN CHAMBERS

Illustrated by Barry Wilkinson

A Piccolo Original

PAN BOOKS LTD

LONDON AND SYDNEY

First published 1974 by Pan Books Ltd,
Cavaye Place, London SW10 9PG

ISBN 0 330 24070 6

Printed and bound in England by
Hazell Watson & Viney Ltd
Aylesbury, Bucks

CONTENTS

From the Author

Ghosts in school, ghosts in pubs, ghosts at sea, ghosts on the Queen's highway, ghosts even in a modern bowling alley; ghosts in Britain are everywhere and appear in broad daylight as well as in the dead of darkest night. These are some of the great British ghosts – apparitions selected from the hundreds to be found in every part of the kingdom.

Frequently in the chapters that follow I have used the words of the people who witnessed the hauntings. At other times I have retold their stories, being careful, though, to see that the essential parts of their evidence are not changed. However, the inclusion of a story does not mean that I accept it as wholly 'true': it doesn't mean that I believe a spirit actually did appear and behave as described – though I do believe that the witnesses *thought* it did! Readers must decide for themselves what they believe. I have simply set down what was reported. I have included these particular stories because I found them both interesting and entertaining. And I hope readers will, too.

I want to thank all those who have written to me after reading my other ghost books – *Haunted Houses*, *More Haunted Houses* and *Great Ghosts of the World*. I enjoyed having their comments and the stories many of them told me. One correspondent, Mr W. V.

Cleveley, sent me such a fascinating account that, with his permission, I have made it into the last chapter of this present volume. Other readers who want to write to me should address their letters to: Aidan Chambers, c/o Piccolo Books, Cavaye Place, London SW10 9PG

A. C.

CHAPTER ONE

The Ghost of Grandpa Bull

Samuel Bull, a chimney-sweep by trade, died in his cottage in Oxford Street, Ramsbury, Wiltshire, in June 1931. For four years he had been ill, nursed by his faithful wife, Mary Jane. But the strain of caring for her husband and her grief at his death finally took their toll. Soon after Samuel's funeral Mary Jane fell ill herself, took to her bed, and remained there, a bedridden invalid for the rest of her days.

Mary Jane's grandson, James Bull, tried to nurse the ailing woman and to keep house and earn a living at the same time. It was a makeshift arrangement that could not last for long. That August, Mrs Edwards,

Grandma Bull's married daughter, moved into her mother's cottage, accompanied by her husband and five children, the eldest of which was a girl of fourteen.

The problem of how to look after Mary Jane was solved. But the solution brought new problems in its wake. Nine people were now packed into the little house in Oxford Street. To make matters worse, the building was badly in need of repair. Shortly after the Edwards family moved in some of the rooms had to be shut up because they were too damp to use. In these unhappy circumstances Mrs Bull and her relatives spent the autumn and winter months.

It was during the February of 1932 that the haunting began.

No doubt as a result of the overcrowded, damp conditions in which they lived, one after another the children fell ill with 'flu, which in those days was still a dangerous sickness. To make them as comfortable as possible and to protect Grandma Bull from infection, three of the children who shared the old woman's bedroom were brought downstairs to the living-room. They had been there a fortnight when, one evening that February, they lay in the candlelight unable to sleep. Someone was lurking outside, they complained. They were quite sure of it, even though neither they nor their mother, who was sitting with them, could hear anyone.

So persistent were the restless children that at last Mrs Edwards opened the door and looked around outside. No one was there; but if she hoped this would settle the children down, she was disappointed. Still they were uneasy – half excited, half fearful, as if expecting the arrival of a strange visitor. This, at least, is how they explained their feelings later, feelings they experienced every time the ghost appeared.

Their instincts had been right. A strange visitor was indeed on its way. Only a short while after Mrs Edwards had looked outside, she and the children were struck dumb when they saw the apparition of Samuel Bull suddenly make itself visible. As they watched in wide-eyed shock, the figure walked up the stairs and entered the room in which the old man had died – one of those the family had recently shut up because of the dampness.

At that moment the children found their voices and screamed. No one can blame them for that. Their grandfather's ghost looked as solid as Samuel Bull had looked in his life, and it was dressed just as he had been when returning home from work each day. But the Edwards children knew very well that Samuel had been dead and buried for eight months past, and that what they saw, therefore, could be nothing other than an ethereal spectre.

We can imagine the flurry of nervous excitement that must have agitated the entire household during the rest of that haunted night. For everyone saw the apparition, and when Grandma Bull heard news of this extraordinary event she was not a bit startled. She had seen the ghost before, she said. She and her family were to see it again, many times.

So frequently did the ghost visit the house, in fact, that the children grew accustomed to its arrival. For about half an hour before anyone could see it, its presence was felt. They all knew the spirit was with them, invisible but unmistakably *there*. Mrs Edwards said she felt at these times 'as though I was expecting my brother from America or something like that'. Then, quite suddenly, the ghost would become visible, as solid-looking and lifelike as any of those watching it.

Always the ghost behaved in the same way. Climbing the stairs, it walked soundlessly to Grandma Bull's room, where it would stand by her bed and lay a hand on the old woman's forehead. The hand, said Mrs Bull, felt firm but cold. And once – only once – she heard the ghost speak. It uttered one word, the name by which Samuel himself had always called his wife: 'Jane'.

These eerie visits were never short, and on at least one occasion lasted several hours. No wonder the family were upset and exhausted each time. They may have grown accustomed to seeing the ghost and lost their fear of it, but they never lost their sense of awe. During the time the ghost was in the house the children would sit unnaturally quiet and still. Nor was there any special hour when the ghost would appear. It was irregular, and might turn up at any time of the day or night. But, just like a living person, it could only be seen at night if a light was burning. Towards the end of the haunting, however, Mrs Edwards said that it began to grow 'lighter', as though it were shining, and then, she said, if the ghost had come in the night she was sure she would have been able to see it in the darkness without the aid of a lamp.

There might have been a reason for this change in the ghost's appearance. Throughout the haunting everyone felt that the ghost was sad. They were quite sure, in fact, that it was worried about Grandma Bull, and the conditions in which she and the family were forced to live. During the haunting news came that a better house had been found for them by the local council. At once the ghost lost its sadness and began to give off the glow Mrs Edwards noted, a glow that could be felt as well as seen by the onlookers and which made them in their turn feel happy. From the time they moved into their new home, the family was left undisturbed by Samuel's apparition.

The ghost of Grandpa Bull was carefully investigated by expert members of the Society for Psychical Research just before the Edwards family moved house. The facts of the haunting were sifted and the possibility of fraud ruled out. But still there was no conclusive answer to the final question that always remains in such otherwise convincing cases: Was the ghost really the spirit of the dead Samuel Bull returning anxiously to watch over his unhappy wife? Or was it an hallucination experienced by everyone who lived in the impoverished conditions of that overcrowded, leaky house? Or was the ghost just a figment of

Grandma Bull's fevered imagination passed by telepathy to each member of the family? Stranger things than this have been known before and since.

CHAPTER TWO

The Ghost and the Pious Woman

Powis Castle in Monmouthshire stands high above the
River Severn, a solid fortress made beautiful by some
of the finest formal gardens in Britain, gardens which
have remained almost unchanged in design since they
were first cultivated two hundred and fifty years ago.
The place is worth a visit, and anyone who goes there
ought to know about its ghost.

In 1780, a poor old woman came to Powis looking for
work. She made her living by spinning, going from
farm to farm in the country round Welshpool, picking
up spinning wherever she could, and staying a day
or two with the farmer's family until the job was

complete. The old woman was known to be very religious, entirely honest and trustworthy, so most of the farmers she called on tried their best to find work for her, whether they really wanted her services or not. On the day she arrived at Powis Castle (known then as Red Castle) the earl was away in London, but his steward, in charge during his master's absence, set the old woman to work.

By nightfall, as she was still busy, the steward's wife told the old woman she could stay till next day, and a room was got ready for her to sleep in. It was a ground floor room with a board floor and two sash windows, grandly furnished with a handsome bed in one corner. The servants had built a good fire to warm the place and in these sumptuous surroundings the old woman, used to a straw mattress in an attic rather than to such luxury, was left to herself for the night. Only when she was alone did she wonder at the steward providing for her so well. And when she came to think of it, she realized the servants who showed her into the room had seemed very keen to be gone as quickly as they could. They did not stop to gossip as servants usually did. Indeed, they had almost dashed out, closing the door firmly behind them. Still, the old woman was used to taking whatever came her way, and life was full of surprises. So she sat herself by the fire and, as was her nightly custom, settled herself to read a chapter of her Bible before going to bed.

She had not been occupied with her religious duties for more than a few minutes when she heard her bedroom door open. Looking up, she was astonished to see a man enter the room, for this was no ordinary man, not one of the servants, but a gentleman, a man of wealth and authority. He wore a gold-laced hat, and his coat and waistcoat and everything else about him were of the finest quality. He walked across the room to the window in the corner and back again to the other window, the bottom of which was chest high. There he stood, half turned towards the old woman, his elbow on the window ledge and his face resting in the palm of his hand. He stayed like this for some time, during which the old woman stared at him, fascinated. She had never seen him before, and all the while she felt that he was waiting for her to speak. But so taken aback was she by his unexpected entry that she could not utter a word. After some while, the gentleman walked off, closing the door behind him.

Shock at the gentleman's arrival gave way now to terror, as the old woman realized that what she had seen was not a man of flesh and blood, but an apparition. The figure had been a ghost, and the servants had known it would appear. That was why they had put her in this grand bedroom, with its fine and comfortable bed. They knew about the ghost and wanted to see what would happen when it confronted a pious old woman. So the old woman guessed – and she was right.

At once she threw herself onto her knees and began praying for help and protection. While she prayed the ghost returned, walked across the room and came close up behind her. Still kneeling, the old woman tried to speak but was so stricken with fear she could not utter a sound. The ghost turned, walked out of the room again, once more closing the door behind it.

Alone for a second time, the old woman managed to calm herself, making up her mind that if the ghost came back she would keep her wits about her and speak to it. Thus resolved, she sat down to await another spectral visitation, her eyes keeping watch on the door.

Sure enough, after only a few moments the door swung open and the ghost entered, walked across the room, and came up behind her just as it had done on its second appearance. Turning her head to face the apparition, the old woman asked as firmly as she could, 'Pray, sir, who are you and what do you want?'

Raising its finger, the ghost replied, 'Take up the candle and follow me, and I will tell you.'

The woman obeyed and followed the ghost out of the room, a candle clutched fearfully in her trembling hand. She was led through a long passage till they reached the door of a room which the ghost opened and passed through. The room was small, hardly bigger than a cupboard. Feeling even more afraid, for she had no wish to be shut in so small a place with a ghost, the old woman stopped at the door. The ghost turned to her and said, 'Walk in. I will not hurt you.'

With the courage only the innocent and faithful possess, the old woman went inside.

'Observe what I do,' said the ghost then.

It stooped and lifted up one of the boards in the floor. Underneath was a box with an iron handle in the lid.

'Do you see that box?' asked the ghost.

'I do,' said the old woman.

The ghost stepped to one side of the room and showed the old woman a crevice in the wall, where it said a key was hidden which would open the box.

'This box and key,' it said, 'must be sent to the earl in London. Will you see it done?'

'I'll do my best,' said the old woman.

'Do, and I will trouble this house no more,' said the ghost, then walked out of the room and disappeared down the passage.

As soon as the old woman saw that the ghost had vanished, she went to the room door and shouted loudly. The steward and his wife and all the other servants ran to her at once; they had been waiting full of curiosity to see what would happen, and now they crowded round the old woman, frightened and full of questions.

The old woman told them all that had taken place and showed the box and key. The steward was afraid to meddle at all, but his wife was less timorous. With the help of some of the servants she hauled the box from its hiding place, took the key from the crevice and carried both off to prepare them for dispatch to the earl.

It would be satisfying to know what that heavy, iron-bound box contained, but the old woman, who told the story to Mr John Hampson, a Methodist preacher, never saw it opened and was never told by anyone what was found inside. All she did know was that on his return from London the earl took the old woman into his care, paying for whatever she wanted – which was never very much – and even offering her rooms of her own at the castle and any comforts she desired to go with them. The old woman, as modest as she was pious, made very few demands on the earl's gratitude. But we can only assume from the earl's behaviour that the box contained such treasure that nothing its finder could ask for in reward could possibly match it in value. As for the ghost, it kept its word as the old woman had kept hers. It has never been seen again.

CHAPTER THREE

A School Haunting

Several young readers have written to me about the
ghosts that are supposed to haunt their schools. A girl
from Worcester told me about her school's first headmistress who was born and died in the building, and
whose spectre is said to walk the classrooms at night
(though how anyone has found that out it would be
interesting to know!). Likewise, I'm told that Sarah
Siddons, the great actress, haunts the school named
after her at Paddington Green, and that another
London school, Marylebone Central, which is built on
the site of an old graveyard, has ghostly visitors in, of
all places, the girls' showers. At another school the

clocktower is said to have been locked up after a prefect had an unpleasant experience there. She was working at a table in the tower one day. Nearby lay a pair of scissors. Suddenly the scissors rose up into the air and passed right through the startled girl – or so the story goes!

The trouble with most accounts of this kind is that there is so little sound evidence to support them. As everyone knows, schoolboys and girls take great pleasure in scaring one another with spinechilling, but entirely invented, tales of horror and suspense. Whether the stories I've mentioned are true or not I cannot say, but one schoolboy ghost story which was carefully examined by various people at the time it happened is persuasive and certainly interesting. It took place many years ago now and concerns the apparition of a boy called John Daniel.

John had been dead more than seven weeks when his ghost was seen by some of his old schoolmates. At that time, in 1728, Beaminster School, Dorset, was held, as many schools were in those days, in a gallery of the local parish church. There was an entrance to the schoolroom leading directly from the churchyard, and every Saturday after class the key to the door was delivered to one of the parish officers by one or other of the children. On Saturday 22 June 1728, the teacher dismissed his pupils as usual. Twelve of the boys then stayed in the churchyard to play football. It was just about midday. After a while four of the boys went back inside the schoolroom to look for pens they had left behind. As they searched, they were startled by a noise in the church, a noise they later described as being like that made by striking a brass pan.

They ran back to their friends in the yard and told them what they had heard. Together they decided that someone was hiding in order to try and frighten them. So all twelve went back into the school gallery to hunt for the culprit. But they could find no one.

As they were walking back down the stairs leading to the yard they heard another noise, this time in the gallery itself. Terrified now, they ran into the church-yard and round the church to the west door. There they stood listening. To their surprise they heard what sounded like someone preaching a sermon. After a short time the preaching was succeeded by the sound of a congregation singing hymns, which also continued for a while before fading away.

All this seemed quite inexplicable, and as nothing else unusual was heard once the singing ended, the boys returned to their game, and soon had forgotten all about this strange event.

A little while later, one of the boys went again into the schoolroom to pick up some belongings. He was stopped in his tracks as he entered the room by the sight of a coffin lying on one of the benches not six feet from him. Not surprisingly, the lad turned tail and fled to the safety of his friends, to whom he gabbled out this new turn in events. The boys thronged to the school door and looked inside. Five of them had a clear view into the schoolroom and each saw not only the coffin but the figure of John Daniel sitting near the coffin but further into the room. The other seven boys, their view partly blocked by the five in front of them, saw only the coffin.

Now John Daniel, as I said earlier, had been dead seven weeks and all but one of the boys who saw his ghost had been to school with him. Amongst them was John's half-brother, and he, seeing the apparition, cried out, 'There sits our John, with just such a coat on as I have, with a pen in his hand, and a book before him and a coffin by him. I'll throw a stone at him.'

The other boys tried to stop him, but he would not listen, saying, as he threw a pebble at the ghost, 'Take that!'

The ghost vanished immediately.

It is easy to imagine the excitement the boys now felt. All twelve had heard the eerie noises and seen the spectral coffin and the unbelievable appearance of a dead friend's ghost. Naturally, they wanted to tell people their story, and soon the whole of Beaminster knew about the goings-on in the schoolroom. No doubt some people dismissed the news as the fanciful imaginings of a few summer-hot children; but there were others, important members of the community, who chose to take the boys seriously. Each was carefully cross-examined by Colonel Broadrep, a local magistrate, and he found that each lad's story agreed closely with the others', even to the detail of the hinges on the coffin lid. The coffin itself was, to judge by the boys' descriptions, exactly like the one in which John Daniel had been buried.

Of course, the boys might have cooked up the entire tale between them. They had known John well, after all, had no doubt attended his funeral, and therefore had seen the coffin as it was borne slowly to its grave. On the other hand, for twelve boys aged between nine and thirteen to stick by a deliberate lie and to make not one slip either in the major details or in their own versions of what happened, even under the kind of repetitive questioning they were subjected to, required rather more tenacity and plain brass-faced self-confidence than any twelve boys can ordinarily muster. One or two together might have pulled it off. But twelve questioned separately by a man like the good Colonel – never! Besides it will be remembered that one of the twelve had never seen John Daniel. This young witness had come to the village after John's death. He was twelve years old and was one of the five who saw John's apparition. He had no memory of the real, living John Daniel to go on. To sustain a lie as detailed as the story told by him and his new schoolfriends he would have to learn a great many facts from the boys who had known John *and be able to repeat them as though he had seen these things at first hand* in reply to questions asked him on his own by the Colonel, questions the boys could not anticipate and so could not specially prepare answers for. Yet during his examination by Colonel Broadrep, this boy, a quiet, gentle fellow by all accounts, gave an exact description of

John Daniel, and mentioned one vital clue not noticed by any of the other boys. One of John's hands, he said, had a white cloth bound round it. When the woman who had prepared the dead John's body for burial was questioned later, she swore on oath that she had removed a white bandage from one of the boy's hands, a fact no one else had mentioned till this time.

We cannot now discover whether the boys saw a ghost or had any kind of psychic experience at all, or were lying. It seems, however, that Colonel Broadrep believed their story, for as a result of his report John Daniel's body was exhumed in order that an inquest could be held on it. John had been found dead about two hundred yards from his home, and had been buried without investigation of that odd circumstance because his mother swore that the boy was subject to fits. Everyone therefore assumed that John had had a fit and had died from it. The inquest now discovered that his death had not been so straightforward. John had, in fact, been strangled. Someone had murdered him.

Did John's ghost return in order to let the world know how he had died? Or had there been talk in the village, rumours that there was more to John Daniel's passing than had been publicly told? And had the boys heard these rumours and then suffered a corporate hallucination as the horror of their friend's death played on their minds? Whatever the answers to these fascinating questions, one fact we are sure about. No one was ever charged with the murder of

John Daniel. The truth of his death was brought to light by the appearance of his ghost in the schoolroom on that bright summer day. But the identity of his killer remains a dark secret even now.

CHAPTER FOUR

Uncle Bert Returns

The majority of apparently true ghost stories are not
spinechilling tales of eerie spectres but brief accounts
told calmly, without fuss, by people who had never
experienced anything so unusual before and quite
often never do again. But these are in some ways the
most interesting of all hauntings, because they happen
to ordinary people in ordinary places. They are over
almost before they begin; but they leave behind vivid,
startling memories, and puzzling questions that remain in the mind long afterwards. Were the visions
really ghosts? Or were they nothing but dreams? Were
they the spirits of dead people suddenly become visible

to the living? Or hallucinations? Or optical illusions? Or tricks played by practical jokers? Or . . . what?

One thing is sure. The percipients – the people who 'see' these short-lived visions – are always quite certain they witnessed something unusual, something not easily explained, something puzzling, awesome, unsettling. Like the family who 'saw' the apparition of Grandfather Bull (see page 9); and like Miss Vivienne Lee of Sale, Manchester, who sent her story to Sir Ernest Bennett, a psychical expert. Sir Ernest included it in his book *Apparitions and Haunted Houses*, which is full of similar fascinating accounts:

I am wondering if an experience which occurred to me when I was nine years of age would be of any interest to you. The impression is as vivid to me today, as it was seventeen years ago.

When I was eight years old, I lost my favourite Uncle. No one explained to me why he failed to come and see us each week as usual. I suppose I have always been a pondering sort of person – I used to wonder if he were happy, and think of him often.

Time passed, and, as is natural at that age, I ceased to worry to the same extent, but often when alone I still questioned where he was; I thought – if only I could see him just once, I would be satisfied.

One morning – about a year later – I was playing with my dolls. I remember just as though it was yesterday – I was kneeling on the floor; one particular doll was in disgrace and I said: 'You will have to leave this class now, and go up there.' At the words 'up there' I glanced upwards – towards the window. I remember dropping the doll, and the words burst from my lips: 'Bunny – Bunny – there is Uncle Bert!' (Bunny was our old maid, who was with me at the time.) Clearly outlined against the wall stood my Uncle.

The strange thing is, and it is difficult to explain just what I mean on paper – time, as such, seemed to cease. My Uncle seemed as though he had always been there, he looked happy – he held out his arms to me, and smiled – telling me not to worry any more.

When I say 'telling me' it again becomes difficult to describe what I mean. He did not speak as we speak – my mind seemed to be in contact with his mind – his lips did not move.

He had not a body like we have; I remember perfectly every detail, much more clearly than I remember physical events of a later date. I could clearly see through his body – the features were the same as before – the outline the same.

The window through which I was looking faced a brick wall; I could see the bricks through my Uncle's form.

He did not move as we move – he seemed to glide, and the form appeared a greyish-white.

I rushed to the door near by, in my efforts to get outside and touch him, but he slowly vanished – into the air.

From that day I was satisfied.

I do not understand it, but I *know* beyond any doubt, I saw my Uncle.

I was certainly not thinking of him at this time, being far too much engrossed with my dolls.

The clearness of this event has never left me.

At Sir Ernest's request, Miss Lee answered some questions in order to make some of what she says clearer:

1. Our old maid Bunny is still alive and though she is bedridden, her mind is quite clear, and on my mentioning the subject to her this morning, she entirely confirms what she said before.

2. As regards the light, this was quite good, although not brilliant sunlight. The incident happened about eleven o'clock in the morning.

3. The figure of my Uncle was outside the window.

4. The room was on the ground floor.

. . . I forget if I told you that our maid was in the pantry, and I in the kitchen, when I saw the figure of my Uncle. Both kitchen and pantry windows face the same brick wall. My Uncle stood between the kitchen window (a large one) and the brick wall, and by the time the maid had rushed from the pantry to the kitchen door, which we were eager to open, in order to run outside, my Uncle was slowly gliding away. Bunny, therefore, did not see his face as I did, though she recognized his figure. The bricks of the wall could be clearly seen through the figure, which was neither grey nor white, but a mixture between the two, and appeared very light. He did not speak, but I clearly understood mentally that he desired me to know that he was well and happy.

Miss Lee also supplied a plan of the house:

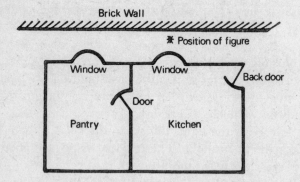

CHAPTER FIVE

The Haunting of Hinton Ampner

Anyone who makes a serious study of ghosts and the places they haunt will sooner or later come across the remarkable story of the twenty-year-long haunting of Hinton Ampner Manor House, which stood near Alresford in Hampshire. And even the most hard-bitten, sceptical investigators find it fascinating. Though the events took place two hundred years ago, the details remain vivid and impressively convincing, because they were carefully recorded by a variety of eye-witnesses, and by one of the ghost's victims in particular, a Mrs Mary Ricketts.

As we must rely on Mrs Ricketts for the best

evidence in the affair, we should look at her closely. She was the daughter of Admiral Jervis, the seaman who fought and won the battle of Cape St Vincent, a victory for which he was rewarded by elevation to the peerage, taking the title Earl St Vincent. Other members of this talented family held high posts in church and government. Mrs Ricketts's husband was William Henry Ricketts, a rich lawyer who owned a great deal of land in the West Indies. Mary herself was held by everyone – relatives, friends, servants – in the deepest respect. She was, they all said, incapable of telling a lie.. Her no-nonsense mind was as sharp as a needle and her willpower and courage impregnable. In fact, she seems to have been a formidable but kindly woman, and as a witness in a case of ghostly activity as reliable as anyone can be. This does not mean, however, that she was incapable of making a mistake about her experiences, or that everything she recorded must be accepted without question. What it does mean is that we can trust that she set down her experiences as honestly and as sincerely as she could manage. The difficult thing is to decide accurately just what caused the events she describes, and whether her interpretations of them are the right ones.

The story begins in 1765 when the Ricketts rented the Manor House. From the time they arrived they heard strange noises. Mrs Ricketts frequently went round the house looking for the cause but never found an explanation. Towards the end of 1769 Mr Ricketts sailed off to Jamaica to attend to his land, leaving his wife, three young children and eight servants at Hinton Ampner. He had not been gone long before the haunting became serious and frightening. Some of the servants left; before the ghost was done with them, all eight had fled and the ones who replaced them never stayed long.

Readers who want to study the various pieces of written evidence will find it in Sacheverell Sitwell's book *Poltergeists* (Faber and Faber) and in the *Journal* of the Society for Psychical Research, vol VI, April 1873. What I have done in the following pages is to take Mrs Ricketts's own account and rewrite it in modern English, so as to remove the archaic language and the repetitive passages. The facts are, of course, unchanged.

The haunting of Hinton Ampner adapted from the account written by Mrs Mary Ricketts

About six months after we came here, Elizabeth Brelsford, who was nanny to our eight-month-old son Henry, was sitting by the baby as he slept in the room over the pantry which we had made into a nursery. It was a hot summer's night so the nursery door had been left open. From where she was sitting, Elizabeth could look across the landing to the door of the yellow bedroom, the one usually occupied by the mistress of the house. As she sat there she saw quite clearly a gentleman dressed in a drab-coloured suit enter the yellow bedroom. She was not at all surprised at the time but when the housemaid, Molly Newman, brought up her supper, Elizabeth asked who the stranger was. When Molly replied that there was no stranger in the house, she described what she had seen. Together the two servants made a search of the bedroom. But they found no one. By this time, Elizabeth was very upset. She was absolutely certain about what she had seen; the light was good enough to distinguish any object clearly.

When I heard Elizabeth's story I dismissed it as superstitious nonsense. I have had to change my opinion since.

In the autumn of the same year, 1765, George Turner, the son of the gardener at that time, while crossing the great hall on his way to bed, saw at the other end a man in a drab-coloured coat. He took him to be the butler, because a new one had just then arrived and had not yet had his livery made. But when George got upstairs to the menservants' dormitory he was astonished to find all of them, including the new butler, in bed. The man in the drab-coloured suit once again could not be accounted for.

In July 1767, at about seven one evening, four of the servants were sitting in the kitchen when they heard a woman coming downstairs, her dress rustling in the way the stiffest silk would. The servants turned to see who the woman might be and saw a tall figure wearing dark-coloured clothes rush past the kitchen door in the direction of the outside entrance to the house. At this moment, the cook was on her way into the kitchen. The figure passed close by her. Startled, the cook and the other servants discussed the incident; and their shocked surprise was heightened when a man coming from the yard into the house from the direction taken by the figure denied having met anyone at all.

Some time after my husband left for Jamaica late in 1769, I frequently heard, as I lay in bed, the noise of someone walking about in my dressing-room next door, and the rustle of silk clothes against the door leading to my bedroom. The noise was sometimes so loud and went on for so long that I could not sleep. Though I often searched the dressing-room as soon as the noises began, I never found anyone there.

After the disturbances had happened a number of times, I made it my practice to search the room and its cupboards and to lock the landing door into the dressing-room from the inside so I could be certain no one could get in without passing through my bedroom. Then I always fastened the door from the dressing-room into my bedroom with a draw-bolt on my side. Even these precautions did not prevent the disturbances, however. They went on uninterrupted.

I was lying awake in the yellow bedroom one night in the summer of 1770 when I heard the plodding tread of a man's footsteps coming towards the foot of my bed. I had been in bed about half an hour, wide awake and without any feelings of fear or apprehension. Now, as the footsteps approached, I thought the danger too close to ring the bell for assistance. Instead I sprang out of bed and ran from the room into the

nursery opposite. Hannah Streeter, who had replaced
Elizabeth as the children's nanny, was in the nursery
and together we took a lamp and searched my room.
But in vain.

This new disturbance upset me greatly, for the
frightening noises were now in my own room, not away
from me safe behind a locked door. Nevertheless, I
plucked up courage and went back to bed without
coming to any conclusion about the cause of the
trouble.

For some months afterwards I heard nothing of any
particular note until the November of the same year.
I had by then moved to a warmer bedroom over the
hall and lying there once or twice heard the sound of
music and, on one night especially, heard three distinct knocks, as though made with a club or something
heavy, against a door downstairs. It occurred to me
that burglars might be trying to break in, but before
I could summon help, the noise ceased and I thought
nothing more of it for the time being. After this, early
in 1771, I was frequently aware of a hollow murmur-
ing noise that seemed to fill the whole house. It was not
made by the wind, as you might expect, because I
heard it on the calmest nights. Besides, I had never
heard it before in all the five years of our living in the
house.

On the morning of 27 February 1771 my maid,
Elizabeth Godin, came into my room, and I inquired
about the weather. She replied in such a faint voice
that I asked if she were ill. No, she said, she was well,

but had never in her life been so terrified as during the past night. She had heard the most evil groans, and fluttering noises round her bed for hours on end. She had got up and searched the room, even looking up the chimney, but though it was a bright, moonlit night, she could find nothing unusual. I said nothing to Elizabeth but hoped she would not find out that the room she slept in had formerly been occupied by Mrs Parfait, the old housekeeper who had died a few days before at Kilmston and had been buried in Hinton churchyard on the evening of the night when this disturbance happened. I knew if Elizabeth discovered this, she would refuse to sleep in the room.

That same day five weeks later, 2 April, I awoke between one and two o'clock (I knew the time because my watch was beside a rushlight on my bedside table.) I lay wide awake for some minutes before I heard people walking about in the passage outside, between my room and the nursery. I got out of bed and listened at the door for about twenty minutes, in which time I distinctly heard the footsteps and also a loud noise like someone pushing hard against a door. By now I was convinced my senses were not playing tricks. So I rang my bell for help, something I had not done at once because I did not want to disturb Hannah Streeter, who was ill with a fever. My maid, Elizabeth Godin, was having to look after Hannah and my three sons too in the nursery.

When Elizabeth came, I asked her if she had seen anyone in the passage. No, she said, she had not. I joined her outside my room. There was a window in the passage which I examined in case someone had gained entrance that way. It was shut tight. We looked under a couch which stood in the passage, the only furniture there that could conceal anyone. The door into the passage was locked, as it ought to have been so that no one could enter our part of the house during the night.

Having thus searched thoroughly, I stood and pondered with much astonishment, when suddenly the door into the yellow room shook as if being rattled to and fro by someone standing behind it.

This was more than I could bear. I ran into the nursery and pulled the bell, which rang in the menservants' quarters. Robert Camis came to the passage door. I let him in, told him why I had summoned him, armed him with a stout stick of wood to use as a club, and waited while he opened the yellow room door.

No one was found. The room was in order and there was no way out.

I dismissed Robert, fastened the door, and went to bed in the nursery, not caring to be on my own again that night, and a little afraid also for Elizabeth. About half an hour later, I heard three clear knocks, just like those earlier. They seemed to come from somewhere below but I could not then or later discover the spot. Next night I slept in my own room and now and then heard noises and often the hollow murmur mentioned before.

On 7 May, exactly five weeks later, the murmur was unusually loud. I could not sleep because of it, all the time expecting something to happen. So I got up and went into the nursery where I stayed until half-past three, and then, when dawn was breaking, went back to my own room, hoping to get some sleep. It was not to be, however, for at ten minutes to four the great hall door directly below me was slammed to with such violence that my room shook from the force of it. I jumped out of bed and ran to the window that over-looked the porch. There was plenty of daylight now, but I saw nothing that could explain the noise. When the door was examined it was found securely locked and bolted as usual.

From this time on I had my maid Elizabeth Godin bring her bed and sleep in my room. The noises grew more frequent, and Elizabeth always heard the same sounds as I, and coming from much the same direction as I thought they did. By now, I was harassed and per-plexed, but very unwilling to tell anyone else of my anxiety. I had taken every possible precaution in hav-ing the house thoroughly investigated but could dis-cover no evidence whatever of trickery. On the contrary, I became convinced the disturbances were beyond the power of any living human being to per-form. But knowing what effect my convictions would have on the rest of the household, I held my tongue.

After midsummer the noises grew worse every night. They began before I went to bed and continued without pause till daybreak. I could often make out voices – usually a shrill female voice to begin with, joined later by two others, deeper, more masculine in tone. But though this conversation seemed to be going on quite close to me, I could never distinguish the words.

Often I asked Elizabeth if she heard any noise. Always she answered by describing exactly what I had heard myself. One night in particular the curtains round my bed rustled as if something had brushed against them. I asked Elizabeth if she had seen anything. Her reply spoke my thoughts!

Several times I heard music – not regular notes or a tune, but a harmonious sound. Every night I heard walking, talking, knocking, the opening and banging closed of doors. My brother, Captain John Jervis, came to stay. But I could not bring myself to discuss these matters with him. They seemed so improbable, so fanciful when spoken of in the calm of the day. The noises went on happening while he was with me, however, and I was naturally curious to know if he heard them too. So one morning I casually said, 'I was afraid last night the servants would disturb you, and rang my bell to order them to bed.'

My brother replied that he had heard nothing!

The night after he left me, at about three o'clock in the morning when daylight was already showing, Elizabeth and I both heard the most loud, deep, tremendous crash, as if some fast-moving object had fallen to the floor with extreme force just outside my room.

We both started up in our beds, Elizabeth looking round her, expecting, as she always did, to see something terrifying.

'Good God!' I cried. 'Did you hear that noise?'

Elizabeth made no reply, so I repeated my question.

'I was that frightened,' she said at last in a faltering voice, 'I scarce dared to speak.'

At this very moment we heard a shrill, dreadful shriek, which seemed to come from under the spot where the falling object fell. The ghastly scream was repeated three or four times, each time fainter than before, as though it were descending slowly into the bowels of the earth.

Lying in the nursery, poor Hannah Streeter heard these noises too, and was so terrified that for two hours she was struck dumb and motionless. To this point, Hannah had heard little of the ghost, and what she had heard she dismissed without giving it much thought. But after this experience, instead of wanting to have no more to do with such strange events, the foolish girl was consumed with curiosity and said she would very much like to hear more of the sounds. Her rash wish was granted. From then until she left the house there was scarcely a night that her sleep was not broken by the sound of footsteps coming towards her door and someone pushing against it as though attempting to force it open.

I was so alarmed myself by this turn of events that I determined to tell my brother about all that was happening when next he visited us. Meanwhile, the constant interruption of my sleep affected my health; I developed a deep cough and a fever.

The morning after my brother at last arrived for his next visit, having warned him that I had something to tell him that would require all his trust in me to believe, I began my story. John listened, surprise and wonder showing on his face. Just as I finished, Captain Luttrell, a neighbour at Kilmston, happened to call, and John told him about the troubles. Together they decided to investigate. We agreed that Captain Luttrell should come to us late that evening, and that my brother and he should divide the night between them, one keeping watch while the other slept. This plan we told to no one else, for obvious reasons.

That evening my brother, accompanied by his man-servant, John Bolton, searched every room in the house, including the attics, looked into every possible hiding place, and made certain each door was locked after him, except those rooms occupied by the family. This done, he went to bed in the room above the servants' hall.

Captain Luttrell and John Bolton, armed with weapons, sat up in the room next to my brother's.

I slept that night in Elizabeth's room, while the children were in the nursery. Thus, every room on that floor was occupied.

As soon as I lay down I heard a rustling as of a person close to the door. I ordered Elizabeth to sit up for a while, and, if the noise continued, to go and tell Captain Luttrell.

Elizabeth heard the noise, and instantly Captain Luttrell's room door was thrown open and we heard him speak.

The Captain told us next morning that he had heard the footsteps of someone walking across the passage. Instantly, he threw open his door.

'Who goes there?' he demanded.

The 'something' flitted past him.

Just then my brother called out, 'Look against my door.'

He too had heard the noise, which seemed to him to be approaching his room. Getting up, he joined the Captain. Both were astonished and now heard various other noises. They looked everywhere but found nothing.

My brother and John Bolton went upstairs to the servants' rooms but found everyone in bed and all the doors secured as they had been earlier. Captain Luttrell and my brother then sat up till daybreak, when my brother returned to his own room.

About this time I heard the door of the Captain's room slam with great violence, and immediately afterwards a door downstairs slammed also. An hour later the main door into the house closed with such force that the building shook to its foundations.

At breakfast that morning I mentioned the doors banging, and was somewhat surprised to learn that Captain Luttrell had thought that it was my door and the one into the room next to mine that had made the row. Odder still, my brother had not heard the doors slamming at all but instead had listened to dreadful groans which he could not explain.

In discussing our restless night on watch, Captain Luttrell said that he believed the disturbances were of such a nature that the house ought not to be lived in. My brother agreed, and we decided to let the owners know what we thought.

Meanwhile, my brother sat up every night for the next week. In the middle of one of these nights I was startled by the noise of a gun going off between my room and the nursery, immediately followed by groaning, as of a person in agony or even dying. The strange thing was that no one else heard these things.

Several more inexplicable noises were heard by different members of the household during the next few days. But never did we discover their cause, and finally my brother returned to Portsmouth, from where he sent his captain of marines to help me pack up and leave Hinton Ampner.

One circumstance more is worth noting: the effect of these events on my favourite cat. She would be sitting quietly on a chair or table when suddenly she would slink down as if terrified, and dive under my chair and put her head close to my feet. A few moments later she would come out and behave calmly again. Never at these times did I see or hear anything that might have alarmed the animal, and I had never seen her act like this before the disturbances began, nor did I ever do so after we left that house. The servants told me that a spaniel dog that lived with them would now and then behave in just this curious manner.

Mrs Ricketts's account of this nerve-wracking haunting was written a year after the events described. Several theories have been put forward since then about the cause of the phenomena. Some people believe the noises were the work of restless, guilty spirits – those of Lord Stawell and his sister-in-law, Honoria, who are supposed to have had a love affair in secret when they lived in the house some years before the Ricketts arrived. A baby was born of this relationship, and, it is said, was murdered to avoid anyone knowing what was going on. That wicked crime left its ghosts to haunt the house, as well it might.

A less horrifying explanation, however, may be quite simply as unspooky as this: about the time of the disturbances, heavy rainfall broke all records and this was followed by extreme frosts, snow, hail and winds. Such entirely natural, even if unusually harsh, conditions could very easily have affected the stability of the building, causing its old timbers to crack, its foundations to move, and what were in effect miniature earthquakes to take place in the ground on which the house stood. Such things have been known to create eerie noises and frightening movements inside buildings and people have thought they were being haunted by ghosts.

This is the trouble with hauntings. Even the most convincing of them may be nothing more than ordinary happenings which are misinterpreted by people who jump too easily to wrong conclusions. On the other hand . . . who knows *beyond doubt*? In cases like Hinton Ampner, no one. Whatever might have caused the troubles, Mrs Ricketts believed till her dying day that she had been the victim of a ghost out haunting.

CHAPTER SIX

A Ghost Pays Its Debts

There are many stories about ghosts who haunt places where treasure is supposed to have been hidden. Most of them are tall tales, entertaining enough but possessing hardly a grain of actual truth. A few, however, are difficult to explain away so easily. One of these was first recorded by a Dr Lee in a famous book, *Glimpses of the Supernatural*. He tells of an old woman called Mrs Webb who died, aged 67, at 2 AM on 3 March 1851, in the village of Barby, Northampton, a place eight miles or so from Rugby and five from Daventry. At that time Barby was small, inhabited by no more than seven hundred people. Everyone knew everyone else.

And Mrs Webb was known as a miser.

She had no need to be. Late in life she married a man who, if he was not wealthy, was certainly well off. He died, leaving all his money and property to his wife. But instead of living comfortably on her small fortune, the widow pinched and scraped and spent as little as she possibly could. Indeed, there were some in the village who said later that her meanness even over her essential needs, let alone her comforts, helped her to an earlier grave than might otherwise have been the case.

At any rate, Mrs Webb eventually fell ill. As she was alone and helpless, two neighbours, Mrs Griffin and Mrs Holding, nursed her. And a nephew, a farmer called Hart, made sure his aunt lacked for nothing and kept an eye on her welfare. Perhaps Mr Hart's thoughtfulness touched his aunt, for when she died she left all her wealth to him. Not that he can have benefited from it immediately, as we shall see.

About a month after the old woman's funeral, Mrs Holding, who lived with her uncle next door to the now empty house, was frightened one night by the noise of loud and heavy thuds against the separating wall. As if that wasn't enough, the door of a cupboard let into the wall was banged on even more violently. At the same time other strange noises were heard, noises like those of furniture being dragged across the floors, even though, as Mrs Holding knew well, there was no furniture left in the house. Everything had been removed so that the house could be let.

Early in April, not long after Mrs Holding's fearful night, a family called Accleton rented Mrs Webb's house from Mr Hart. In Dr Lee's own words taken from his report of the haunting, this is what happened next:

The husband was often absent, but he and his wife occupied the room in which Mrs Webb had died, while their daughter, a girl of about ten years of age, slept in a small bed in the corner. Violent noises in the night were heard about two o'clock – thumps, tramps, and tremendous crashes, as if all the furniture had been collected together and then violently banged to the floor. One night at 2 AM the parents were suddenly awakened by the violent screams of the child.

'Mother! Mother! There's a tall woman standing by my bed, a-shaking her head at me!'

The parents could see nothing, so did their best to quiet and compose the child. At four o'clock they were awakened by the child's screams, for she had seen the woman again; in fact, she appeared to her no less than seven times on seven subsequent nights.

If Mrs Accleton thought her daughter's troubles were nothing worse than nightmares brought on by the strange noises, she soon changed her mind. One night during her husband's absence, it was she and not her young daughter who was woken at two o'clock. An eerie light had disturbed her. Looking up from her pillow she clearly saw the ghost of Mrs Webb coming towards her. And as it came it silently made pleading movements, as though trying to say 'Speak! Speak!'

Quite understandably, Mrs Accleton had very soon recounted every detail of this nerve-shattering event to her neighbours. Three of them must have agreed to keep her company at night while her husband was away from home. However it came about, Mrs Holding, Mrs Griffin and a Mrs Radbourne also became witnesses of the vision. They claimed a ball of light rose into the air towards a trapdoor in the ceiling. The trapdoor gave entrance into the unused loft formed by the pitch of the roof. At the same time, said the women, they heard a low, unearthly, moaning sound, 'strange and unnatural like', but similar to the moans made by old Mrs Webb in her final moments of life.

What could these astonishing disturbances mean? Why did the ghost make such pleading gestures? Why did the luminous sphere rise towards the trapdoor? The four women discussed such questions with the intense interest of those who have taken part in momentous events. It was Mrs Accleton who first suggested that the ghost might be trying to communicate a message. And that the message was about something hidden in the loft. Following this line of thought, it wasn't long before Mrs Webb's reputation as a miser led the women to the conclusion that her ghost wanted to tell them money was hidden in the roof. Sure they had the answer to the puzzle, off the women went to Mr Hart.

We do not know how Mr Hart reacted when he first heard what the women had to say. But we do know they eventually convinced him sufficiently to make him agree to search the loft. Accompanied by Mrs Accleton, and lighting their way with a candle, he climbed through the trapdoor into the dark, triangular and dusty space between ceiling and roof. We can now only imagine, for they were never recorded, what feelings of amazement and awe overcame the search party when first they discovered a bundle of old deeds relating to Mrs Webb's property, and then a large bag. The bag was stuffed full of gold coins and bank notes. Mr Hart had come into his inheritance at last.

Everyone expected that the haunting would now cease. But it did not. The ghost had other ideas than simply to make Mr Hart wealthy. The knockings and moanings and strange noises went on unabated. Meanwhile, certain unpaid bills came to light. Slow to give her money away, even in payment of debts, Mrs Webb had departed this life leaving behind a number of unsatisfied creditors. Mr Hart set about paying off every claim scrupulously. And only then did the ghost cease its nightly activities in the bedroom where Mrs Webb had died. So it seems that in the end Mrs Webb had a conscience. She may have been a skinflint, but she wasn't a thief. And from her grave she made certain that whatever she owed was finally paid in full.

CHAPTER SEVEN

Lighting the Way to the Grave

In some parts of the country people believe that spirits of a dying man's dead friends rise from their graves in the form of ghostly lights, like spectral candles, and welcome his soul into the next world. Whether or not this is scientifically true, or simply folklore without any basis in fact, a great many stories have grown up around it. Stories like the one told by the Reverend S. Baring-Gould, the Church of England priest who wrote the hymn *Onward Christian Soldiers*.

A minister new to a country parish, his story goes, was leaning on the churchyard wall one evening when he saw a light suspended in the air above a particular spot. His first thought was that someone with a lantern must be in the churchyard. So he opened the gate and went in to find out who this person was. However, before he reached the light, it moved away from him. He followed, all the more puzzled now because he could not see anyone, though he had come close enough to have done so were anyone there. The light never rose very far above the ground but travelled quite fast out of the churchyard, across a road, through a wood, and up a hill, till it reached the door of a farmhouse, where it disappeared.

The minister's curiosity was by this time thoroughly aroused. For a while he stood wondering whether or not he should call at the house so late in the evening to inquire about the strange light. But before he could make up his mind the light reappeared, accompanied by another. Together, they glided past the fascinated priest, retraced the path to the churchyard, and then both vanished at the grave where the priest had seen the first light hovering. Determined to investigate, the vicar left a mark on the grave so that he would be able to identify the spot with certainty next day.

In the morning, the priest discovered from the sexton that the grave was owned by a family who lived up the hill behind the wood. But, said the sexton, no one had been buried in it for a very long time.

Later that same day, the vicar was called to this very farmhouse. We can only imagine how surprised and shocked he was to be told that the previous evening, while he stood outside pondering on the peculiar light, a child in the family had died of scarlet fever.

Baring-Gould, a priest himself, was perhaps deeply impressed by the ghost-candle belief and this touching story. (Was he the vicar in the story, I wonder?) At any rate, he wrote a poem about the incident:

The Little Blue Flame

All under the stars, and beneath the green tree,
All over the sward, and along the cold lea,
   A little blue flame a-fluttering came;
It came from the churchyard for you or for me.

I sit by the candle, my baby's asleep,
And rocking the cradle, I wonder and weep.
   O little blue light in the dead of the night,
O prithee, O prithee, no nearer to creep.

Why follow the church-path, why steal you this way?
Why halt in your journey, on the threshold to stay?
   With flicker and flare, why dance up the stair?
O I would! O I would! it were dawning of day.

All under the stars, and along the green lane,
Unslaked by the dew, and unquenched by the rain,
   Of little flames blue to the churchyard steal two.
The soul of my baby! now from me is ta'en.

CHAPTER EIGHT

Black Shuck and Other Animal Ghosts

Animals as well as people have their ghosts, if the many stories about animal apparitions are to be believed. Ghostly dogs are most numerous, cropping up all over Britain, usually described as 'black, large, and shaggy with long ears and tails', and frequently associated with evil and death. In each locality these dogs of doom have a name. The Welsh talk of their 'Gwyllgi' – a terrifying mastiff-like creature with blazing eyes. On the Isle of Man the Manx have their 'Mauthe' dog, a sort of long-haired spaniel, one of which haunts Peel Castle. The Peel Castle Mauthe has his milder side, however; he is seen at times going into the guardroom, where he lies down and warms himself by the fire.

'Monstrous human-headed dogs, black, with fiery eyes and teeth sprinkled all over with blood' are supposed to hunt in a pack in Cornwall, where they are called 'the Devil and his Dandy dogs'. A similar pack hunts in the north of England. Called 'Gabriel's hounds', this canine mob chases after its victim, yelping, so terrifying the unfortunate human that his soul takes leave of his body.

In Lancashire the phantom dog is called 'Trash', because the noise its feet make is like someone walking through sloppy mud, or 'Shriker', because of the screaming sound it makes when someone is about to die. Around Leeds in Yorkshire people call their black dog 'Padfoot' and say it is almost the size of a donkey, covered in mangy hair and with saucer-like eyes. In the Hebrides the death-dog is white, not black, runs round in circles to warn of an approaching death, and is called 'Lamper'.

Sometimes these spectral beasts are believed to house the spirits not of animals but of dead men. In other words, they are human ghosts which take a dog-like shape, as in this story from Hertfordshire: An old woman suspected of witchcraft in a small village near Tring was drowned in 1751. A local sweep was blamed for the old woman's death, and was tried and hanged near the place where he committed the murder. Long afterwards the spot was said to be haunted by a big black dog which everyone believed was the sweep's ghost 'in disguise'. The village schoolteacher once met the spectre, and wrote an account of what he saw:

I was returning home late at night in a gig with the parson driving, and when we came to the spot where the gibbet had stood, we saw on the bank of the roadside a flame as large as a man's hat.

'What's that?' I exclaimed.

'Hush!' said my companion, and suddenly pulling in his horse, came to a stop.

I then saw an immense black dog just in front of the horse, the strangest looking creature I ever beheld. He was as big as a Newfoundland, but very gaunt, shaggy with long ears and tail, eyes like balls of fire and large long teeth, for he opened his mouth and seemed to grin at us.

In a few minutes the dog disappeared and vanished like a shadow or sank into the earth.

An even more frightening story, because the narrator was attacked by the ghosts – a human apparition this time as well as one in the shape of a dog – was told to a famous newspaper journalist, Mr W. T. Stead, when he was editor of *The Northern Echo*. Mr Stead included the tale in an article called 'Real Ghost Stories', published in the magazine *Review of Reviews*.

I was night watchman at the old Darlington and Stockton Station at the town of Darlington, a few yards from the first station that ever existed. I was there fifteen years. I used to go on duty about 8 PM and come off at 6 AM. I had been there a little while – perhaps two or three years – and about forty years ago. One night during winter at about twelve o'clock or twelve thirty, I was feeling rather cold with standing here and there; I said to myself, 'I will away down and get myself something to eat.' There was a porter's cellar where a fire was kept on and a coalhouse was connected with it. So I went down the steps, took off my overcoat, and had just sat down on the bench opposite the fire and turned up the gaslight when a strange man came out of the coalhouse, followed by a big black retriever. As soon as he entered, my eye was upon him, and his eye upon me, and we were intently watching each other as he moved on to the front of the fire. There he stood looking at me, and a curious smile came over his countenance. He had a stand-up collar and a cut-away coat with gilt buttons and a Scotch cap. All at once he struck at me, and I had the impression that he hit me. I up with my fist and struck back at him. My fist seemed to go through him and struck against the stone above the fireplace, and knocked the skin off my knuckles. The man seemed to be struck back into the fire, and uttered a strange, unearthly squeak. Immediately the dog gripped me by the calf of my leg, and seemed to cause me pain. The man recovered his position, called off the dog with a sort of click of the tongue, then went back into the coalhouse, followed by the dog. I lighted my dark lantern and looked into the coalhouse, but there was neither dog nor man, and no outlet for them except by the one which they had entered.

I was satisfied that what I had seen was ghostly, and it accounted for the fact that when the man had first come into the place where he sat I had not challenged him with any inquiry. Next day, and for several weeks, my account caused quite a commotion, and a host of people spoke to me about it; among the rest old Edward Pease, father of railways, and his three sons, John, Joseph and Henry. Old Edward sent for me to his house and asked me all particulars. He and others put this question to me: 'Are you sure you were not asleep and had the nightmare?' My answer was quite sure, for I had not been a minute in the cellar, and was just going to get something to eat. I was certainly not under the influence of strong drink, for I was then, and I have been for forty-nine years, a teetotaller. My mind at the time was perfectly free from trouble. What increased the excitement was the fact that a man a number of years before, who was employed in the office of the station, had committed suicide, and his body had been carried into this very cellar. I knew nothing of this circumstance, nor of the body of the man, but Mr Pease and others who had known him, told me my description exactly corresponded to his appearance and the way he dressed, and also that he had a black retriever just like the one which gripped me. I should add that no mark or effect remained on the spot where I seemed to be seized.

James Durham

December 9, 1890

The retriever seen by Mr Durham was obviously not the legendary 'black dog' of death. But there is one in the Darlington and County Durham area. It is called a 'Barguest', and a favourite haunt was in a glen near Throstlenest, which lies between Darlington and the village of Haughton (now almost completely absorbed into the town by new buildings). I lived near Throstlenest during my teens and often went walking in that district, but never met the Barguest!

Undoubtedly the best known of these hell-hounds, however, is 'Black Shuck', which inhabits the flat lands of Norfolk and the fens. 'Shuck' is a name that comes from the Anglo-Saxon word *Scucca* or *Sceocca*, meaning Satan – the Devil. It is as big as a half-grown calf and lurks in hedgerows, using the cover to track lonely travellers whom it ambushes and scares to death with its single glaring eye. Neatishead Lane near Barton Broad is said to be a favourite spot of Black Shuck, as is Coltishall Bridge, which it crosses. It also seems to like walking along the road from Beeston, near Sherringham, to Overstrand.

Mr W. A. Dutt wrote about this monstrous phantom in *Highways and Byways of East Anglia*:

It is not the children only who go about at night in fear of Black Shuck. If this were a stormy night instead of a stormy day, the old fisherfolk of the coast would say it was just the time for Black Shuck to be abroad; for he revels in the roaring of the waves and loves to raise his awful voice above the howling gale. Black Shuck is the 'Moddey Doo' of the Norfolk coast.

He takes the form of a huge black dog and prowls along dark lanes and lonesome field-paths, where, although his howling makes the hearer's blood run cold, his footfalls make no sound. You may know him at once, should you see him, by his fiery eye; he has but one, and that, like the Cyclops, is in the middle of his head. But such an encounter might bring you the worst of luck; it is even said that to meet him is to be warned that your death will occur before the end of the year. So you will do well to shut your eyes if you hear him howling – shut them even if you are uncertain whether it is the dog-fiend or the voice of the wind you hear.

An old woman was walking home one night from Gillingham to Geldeston when she met Black Shuck. She was with Josh, then her husband-to-be, and she told her story many years later to Mr Morley Adams, who included it in his book, *In the Footsteps of Barrow and Fitzgerald*:

It was after I had been promised to Josh and before we were married that I saw the 'Hateful Thing' ...

It was between eight and nine and we were in a lane near Geldeston when we met Mrs S. and she started to walk with us, when I heard something behind us, like the sound of a dog running. I thought that it was some farmer's dog, and paid little attention to it, but it kept on just at the back of us, pit-pat-pit-pat-pit-pat!

'I wonder what that dog wants?' I said to Mrs S.

'What dog do you mean?' said she, looking all round.

'Why, can't you hear it?' I said. 'It has been following us for the last five minutes or more! You can hear it, can't you, Josh?' I said.

'Nonsense, old mawther,' said Josh, 'just you lug hold of my arm and come along.'

I was walking between Josh and Mrs S. and I lay hold of Mrs S.'s arm and she says, 'I can hear it now; it's in front of us; look, there it be!'

And sure enough just in front of us was what looked like a big, black dog; but it wasn't a dog at all; it was the 'Hateful Thing' that had been seen hereabouts before and it betokened some great misfortune.

It kept in front of us until it came to the churchyard, when it went right through the wall and we saw it no more.

Not to be outdone by the dogs, cats make ghostly appearances now and again. But they are usually not so fierce and evil-seeming. A friend of mine, who lives in a haunted house, once experienced the eerie sensation of an invisible cat jumping onto his lap as he sat at the breakfast table. The animal turned round twice before curling up on his knees. There was nothing to be seen; but he clearly felt the creature's treading paws and the balanced weight so characteristic of the feline species. When the initial shock at this unexpected visit had died away, he instinctively tried to push the cat off his lap. His hands felt the curving back and smooth soft fur, just as though a solid body was there. And as he pushed, the ghostly creature stood up and jumped from his knees.

Several years ago in the *Occult Review* letters were published describing ghost-cat appearances. Two of these accounts are typical of many others. The first is a haunting experienced by three people, each of whom relates what she saw. (The witnesses have been given pen names to hide their identity.)

'Thanet's' story:
One evening, about four years ago I was in my drawing-room with two friends; we were all standing up on the point of going to bed, and only waiting till the old Cook had succeeded in inducing the grey Persian cat to come in for the night. This was sometimes difficult, and then Cook came up as on this occasion and called him from the balcony, and the french window was wide open, when a cat rushed in at the window and through the door.

'What was that?' we said, looking at one another. It was not Kitty, the grey Persian, but darker, and was it really a cat, or what? My friend 'Rugen' has written the account of what she saw before seeing what I have said. 'Iona' confirms our description. What I saw seemed dark and shadowy and yet unmistakably a cat. It seemed to me like the predecessor of Kitty, which was a black Persian; he had the same habit of coming in at night by this window, and he constantly rushed through the room, and downstairs, being in a hurry for his supper. A moment or two afterwards the grey cat walked slowly in, and though we searched the house, we could find no other.

'Rugen's' story, part one:
Three or four years ago 'Iona' and I were sitting in the drawing-room on a Sunday evening, when Cook came in to ask for Kitty (a silver-grey Persian cat) to settle him in the kitchen for the night. Kitty was still in the garden, and Cook went to the balcony calling him.

Suddenly I saw a black cat flying in and disappearing behind or under a seat. First, I did not take much notice of this. But when a minute after, Kitty slowly and solemnly stepped in, followed by Cook, it struck me that the dark something could not have been Kitty, and 'Thanet' and 'Iona' made the remark simultaneously. Now we began to look for the dark one all over the place without any result. Cook had not seen any cat passing her on the balcony except Kitty the grey one. 'Thanet' had had a black Persian cat, which died before Kitty came.

'Iona's' witness:
I can entirely corroborate the accounts written by 'Thanet' and 'Rugen'.

I remember that I saw something like a dark shadow move very quickly and disappear in front of a cottage piano. I exclaimed simultaneously with my friends, 'What was that?' and shared their surprise when no black cat was found, and the grey Persian walked in unconcernedly through the open window.

'Rugen's' story, part two:
Cook said, 'I wish you would come downstairs and see how strangely Kitty behaves as soon as I open the cupboard. There is nothing in it but the wood; I turned it all out to see what might be the reason – not even a mousehole can I find.'

Some days previously Cook had told me that nothing could induce Kitty to sleep in his basket, and one day he would not eat any food in the kitchen, and his meals had to be given him outside. So I went down, to please Cook. Kitty was picked up, and while Cook petted and stroked him, she knelt down and opened the cupboard. Kitty, stretching his neck and looking with big, frightened eyes into the cupboard's corner, suddenly turned round; struggling out of Cook's hold and rushing over her shoulder, he flew out of the kitchen. Getting up, Cook said: 'That's always what he does, just as if he was seeing something horrible!'

Next day I encouraged Cook to talk of Ruff, the former black cat, which had been a great favourite of hers, and which she had been nursing when he was dying. 'Oh, poor thing, when he was ill, he would creep into dark corners, so I put him in his basket into the cupboard, making it very comfortable for him, and there he died' – pointing to the very corner which caused such horror to Kitty.

Kitty's reactions to whatever he saw are typical of the way animals have been known to behave in haunted places. Can animals see visions which remain invisible to most people? Perhaps. But no one has yet been able to prove it.

The second narrative involves a ghostly old man as well as a cat, and was signed once again with a pen name, 'Munster'.

My son had the following experience at the age of four years in our Worcestershire home.

He was an only child and spent much of his time in the company of a cat who shared his tastes and pursuits even to the extent of fishing in the River Weir with him, the cat being far more proficient at the sport than the boy. When the cat died we none of us dared to break the news to the child, and were much surprised when he asked us to say why his cat only came to play with him at nights nowadays. When we questioned him about it, he stoutly maintained that his cat was there in bodily form every night after he went to bed, looking much the same but a little thinner.

At about the same age, one evening after being in bed one hour, I heard him cry out, and going upstairs (his maid also heard and ran up) and asking him what was the matter, he said that an old gentleman with a long grey beard like his grandfather came into his room, and stood at the foot of his bed. At that very moment, the former had a seizure in his carriage while driving through the streets of Birmingham, from which he died without regaining consciousness; later on he recognized a photograph of his grandfather as being the person he saw at the foot of his bed. My wife, the maid and myself can vouch for the accuracy of these statements, also friends to whom we have related these facts.

If the little boy really did see these ghosts, and did not invent them or dream them, then he must have been a 'sensitive' – one of those people with the gift of 'seeing' psychic phenomena. Certainly, the two ghosts he saw, the cat and the old man, are classic examples of two kinds of spectre frequently experienced and often recorded.

Horses inhabit the ghost world in fairly large numbers, too. Mostly they are being ridden or are pulling carriages. Mr W. T. Stead collected this example from a leading citizen of Cowes in the Isle of Wight:

On a fine evening in April, 1859, the writer was riding with a friend on a country road. Twilight was closing down on us, when, after a silence of some minutes, my friend suddenly exclaimed:

'No man knows me better than you do, J. Do you think I am a nervous, easily frightened sort of man?'

'Far from it,' said I, 'among all the men I know in the wild country I have lived and worked in, I know none more fearless or of more unhesitating nerve.'

'Well,' said he, 'I think I am that, too, and though

I have travelled these roads all sorts of hours, summer and winter, for twenty years, I never met anything to startle me, or that I could not account for, until last Monday evening. About this time it was. Riding old Fan' – a chestnut mare – 'here on this crossroad, on my near side was a man on a grey horse, coming from this left-hand road. I had to pull my off-rein to give myself room to pass ahead of him; he was coming at a right angle to me. As I passed the head of the horse I called out, "Good night". Hearing no reply, I turned in my saddle to the off-side, to see whether he appeared to be asleep as he rode, but to my surprise I saw neither man nor horse. So sure was I that I had seen such, that I wheeled old Fan round, and rode back to the middle of the cross, and on neither of the four roads could I see a man or horse, though there was enough light to see two hundred or three hundred yards, as we can now. Well then I rode over that gate' – a gate at one corner opening into a grass field – 'thinking he might have gone that way; looking down by each hedge, I could see nothing of my man and horse; and then – and not till then – I felt myself thrill and start with a shuddering sense that I had seen something uncanny, and, Jove! I put the mare down this hill we are on now at her very best pace.

'But the strangest part of my story is to come,' said he, continuing. 'After I had done my business at the farmhouse here, at foot of this hill, I told the old farmer and his wife what I had seen, as I have told you. The old man said:

' "For many years I have known thee, M——, on this road, and have you never seen the like before on that cross?"

' "Seen what before?" I said.

' "Why, a man in light-coloured clothes on a grey horse," he said.

' "No, never," said I, "but I swear I have this evening."

'The farmer asked, "Did you ever hear of what happened to the miller of L—— Mills about forty years ago?"

' "No, never a word," I told him.

' "Well," he said, "about forty years ago this miller, returning from market, was waylaid and murdered on that crossroad, pockets rifled of money and watch. The horse ran home, about a mile away. Two serving-men set out with lanterns and found their master dead. He was dressed, as millers often do in this part of the country, in light-coloured clothes, and the horse was a grey horse. The murderers were never found. These are facts," continued the farmer. "I took this farm soon after it all happened, and, though I have known all this, and have passed over that cross several thousands of times, I never knew anything unusual there myself, but there have been a number of people who tell the same story you have told mother and me, M——, and describe the appearance as you have done to us tonight." '

In December 1907, the *Occult Review* published an

article called 'Some More Welsh Ghosts' in which the author, Mary L. Lewes, told the following story:

In common with several other districts in Great Britain and Ireland, Pembrokeshire possesses a good 'phantom coach' legend, localized in the southern part of the county, at a place where four roads meet, called Sampson Cross. In the old days the belated farmer driving home in his gig from market was apt to cast a nervous glance over his shoulder as his pony slowly climbed the last pitch leading to the Cross. For tradition says that every night a certain Lady Z (who lived in the seventeenth century, and whose monument is in the church close by) drives over from Tenby, ten miles distant, in a coach drawn by headless horses, guided by a headless coachman. She also has no head, and arriving by midnight at Sampson Cross, the whole equipage is said to disappear in a flame of fire, with a loud noise of explosion.

Such phantom carriages are common enough, as Mary Lewes says, and some have been carefully investigated and recorded, like the one seen at the house of a Major W— near Conon Bridge, Ross-shire, Scotland, on 23 August 1878, as the Major himself described:

It was rather a dark night and very still. It had struck midnight, when, before retiring for the night, I went, as is often my custom, to the front door to look at the weather. When standing for a moment on the step, I saw coming round a turn in the drive a large closed carriage and a pair of horses with two men on the box. It passed the front of the house and was going at a rapid rate towards a path which leads to a stream, running at that point between rather steep banks.

There is no carriage road on that side of the house and I shouted to the driver to stop, as if he went on he must undoubtedly come to grief. The carriage stopped abruptly when it came to the running water, turned and in doing so drove over the lawn.

I got up to it, and by this time my son had joined me with a lantern.

Neither of the men on the box had spoken and there was no sound from the inside of the carriage.

My son looked in and all he could discern was a stiff-looking figure inside, sitting up in a corner and draped apparently from head to foot in white. The absolute silence of the men outside was mysterious and the white figure inside, apparently of a female, not being alarmed or showing any sign of life was strange.

Men, carriage and horses were unknown to me, although I know the country so well.

The carriage continued its way across the lawn, turning up a road which led past the stables and so into the drive again and away. We could see no traces of it the next morning, and no mark of wheels or horses' feet on the soft grass or gravel road.

My wife and daughter also saw the carriage, being attracted to the window by my shout.

* * *

Animal ghosts and phantom carriages bearing the spirits of the dead are all summed up in the chilling legend of the Death Coach, a story common in Devon and Wales. This dreadful vehicle, black all over, is pulled by black horses driven by a headless coachman. Before it, runs a black hound-dog, and inside sits a lady – not a lady dressed in white such as the Major gazed upon, but a black-clad figure said by those who live around Okehampton and Tavistock to be the ghost of one Lady Howard, who, in the sixteenth century, had four husbands, each of whom she murdered! Whoever this gloomy person is, the legend says that her coach travels the countryside, picking up along the way the souls of the dying, which it carries off to Hell.

> Now pray step in! my lady saith;
> > Now pray step in and ride.
> I thank thee, I had rather walk
> > Than gather to thy side.

> The wheels go round without a sound
> > Or tramp or turn of wheels.
> As cloud at night, in pale moonlight,
> > Along the carriage steals.

> I'd rather walk a hundred miles
> > And run by night and day,
> Than have that carriage halt for me,
> > And hear my lady say –

Now pray step in, and make no din,
    Step in with me to ride;
There's room, I trow, by me for you,
    And all the world beside.

The Ghost Aboard HMS Asp

The following record of an extraordinary haunting aboard the Admiralty survey vessel, HMS *Asp*, was written by the ship's commander, Captain Aldridge, RN, and published as a letter to the *Pembroke County Guardian*. The letter was dated 15 March 1867. Over thirty years later, seamen in Pembroke dock were still talking about the events described, and so the newspaper reprinted the Captain's account on 16 February 1901. Even so short a time as twenty years ago there were still Pembroke people who remembered the affair. Such was the effect of this naval ghost.

15 March 1867.

My dear Sir,

I herewith readily comply with your request as far as I am able, respecting the unaccountable 'apparition' on board my ship. Call it ghost or what you will, still I assure you that which I am going to relate is what really did take place, and much as I was, and am, a sceptic in ghost stories, I must confess myself completely at a loss to account by natural causes for that which did actually occur. Many years having elapsed since I retired from active service, I am unable to recollect all the dates with exactness, but I will give them as far as I can remember them.

In the year 1850, the *Asp* was given me by the Admiralty as a surveying vessel. On taking possession of her, the Superintendent of the Dockyard where she lay remarked to me, 'Do you know, sir, your ship is said to be haunted, and I don't know if you will get any of the Dockyard men to work on her.' I, of course, smiled, and I said, 'I don't care for ghosts, and dare say I shall get her all to rights fast enough.'

I engaged the shipwrights to do the necessary repairs to the vessel, but before they had been working in her a week they came to me in a body and begged me to give the vessel up as she was haunted and could never bring anything but ill-luck. However, the vessel was at length repaired, and arrived in safety in the River Dee, where she was to commence her labours. After my tea in the evening, I generally sat in my cabin and either read to myself or had an officer of mine (who is now master of the *Magician*) to read aloud to me: on such occasions we used frequently to be interrupted by strange noises, often such as would be caused by a drunken man or a person staggering about, which appeared to issue from the after (or ladies') cabin.

The two cabins were only separated from each other by the companion ladder, the doors facing each other, so that from my cabin I could see into the after one. There was no communication between either of them and the other parts of the ship, excepting by the companion ladder, which no one could ascend or descend without being seen from my cabin. The evening shortly after our arrival in the Dee, the officer I mentioned was reading to me in my cabin when all at once his voice was drowned by a violent and prolonged noise in the aft cabin. Thinking it must be the steward he called out, 'Don't make such a noise, steward,' and the noise ceased. When he began to read again the noise also recommenced. 'What are you doing, steward – making such a noise for?' he cried out, and taking the candle hastened into the next cabin. But he came back quicker than he went, saying there was nobody there.

He recommenced reading, and once more began the mysterious noise. I felt sure there was some drunken person there whom my officer had overlooked, and accordingly rose and looked myself, and to my very disagreeable surprise found the cabin empty!

After this evening, the noises became very frequent, varying in kind and in degree. Sometimes it was as though the seats and lockers were being banged about, sometimes it sounded as though decanters and tumblers were being clashed together. During these disturbances the vessel was lying more than a mile off shore.

One evening I and the above named officer went to drink tea at a friend's house at Queen's Ferry, near Chester, the vessel at the time being lashed to the lower stage opposite Church's Quay. We returned on board together about 10 PM. While descending the companion ladder, I distinctly heard someone rush from the after cabin into the fore cabin. I stopped the officer who was behind me at the top of the ladder and whispered to him, 'Stand still, I think I have caught the ghost.'

I then descended into my cabin, took my sword, which always hung over my bed, and placed it drawn in his hand saying, 'Now, allow no one to pass you; if anyone attempts to escape cut him down, I will stand the consequences.'

I then returned to the cabin, struck a light and searched everywhere, but nothing could I find to account for the noises I had heard, though I declare solemnly that never did I feel more certain of anything in my life than that I should find a man there. So there was nothing to be done but to repeat for the hundredth time, 'Well, it is the ghost again!'

Often when lying in my bed at night I heard noises close to me as though drawers were being opened and shut, the top of my washing-stand raised and banged down again, and a bed which stood on the opposite side of my cabin, pulled out; while of an evening I often heard while sitting in my cabin a noise as though a percussion cap were snapped close to my head; also very often (and I say it with godly and reverential fear) I have been sensible of the presence of something invisible about me, and could have put my hand, so to say, on it, or the spot where I felt it was; and all this occurred, strange to say, without my feeling in the least alarmed or caring about it, except so far that I could not understand or account for what I felt and heard.

One night, when the vessel was at anchor in Martyn Roads, I was awoken by the quartermaster, who called me and begged me to come on deck as the look-out man had rushed to the lower deck, saying that a figure of a lady was standing on the paddle box pointing with her finger to Heaven. Feeling angry, I told him to send the look-out man on deck again and keep him there till daybreak, but in attempting to carry my orders into execution the man went into violent convulsions, and the result was I had to go myself upon deck and remain there till morning.

This apparition was often seen after this, and always as described with her finger pointing towards Heaven.

One Sunday afternoon while lying in the Haverford-west River opposite Lawrenny, the crew being all on shore, and I being at church, my steward (the only man on board) whilst descending the companion ladder was spoken to by a voice although there was nobody else to be seen. He immediately fell down with fright, and I found his appearance so altered that I really scarcely knew him!

He begged to be allowed his discharge and to be landed as soon as possible, to which I felt obliged to consent as he could not be persuaded to remain on board for the night.

The story of the ship being haunted becoming known on shore, the clergyman of Lawrenny called on me one day and begged me to allow him to question the crew, which he accordingly did. He seemed very much impressed by what he heard; he seemed to view the matter in a serious light and said that his opinion was that 'some troubled spirit must be lingering about the vessel'.

During the years that I commanded the *Asp* I lost many of my men who ran away on being refused their discharge, and a great many others I felt forced to let go, so great was their fear, one and all telling the same tale, namely that at night they saw the transparent figure of a lady pointing with her finger up to Heaven. For many years I endeavoured to ridicule the affair as I was often put to considerable inconvenience by the loss of hands, but to no purpose. I believe that when the officers went out of the vessel after dark, none of the crew would have ventured into the cabin on any account.

One night I was awoken from my sleep by a hand, to all sensations, being placed on my leg outside the bedclothes. I lay still for a moment to satisfy myself of the truth of what I felt, and then grabbed at it, but caught nothing. I rang the bell for the quartermaster to come with his lantern, but found nothing.

This occurred to me several times, but on one occasion as I lay wide awake a hand was placed on my forehead. If ever a man's hair stood on end mine did then. I sprang clean out of bed: there was not a sound. Until then I had never felt the least fear of the ghost or whatever you like to call it. In fact I had taken a kind of pleasure in listening to the various noises as I lay in bed, and sometimes when the noises were very loud I would suddenly pull my bell for the look-out man and then listen attentively if I could hear the sound of a footstep or attempt to escape, but there never was any, and I would hear the look-out man walk from his post to my cabin when I would merely ask him questions as to the wind and weather.

At length, in 1857, the vessel, requiring repairs, was ordered alongside the dockyard wall at Pembroke. The first night the sentry stationed near the ship saw (as he afterwards declared) a lady mount the paddle box holding up her hand towards Heaven. She then stepped on shore and came along the path towards him when he brought his musket to the charge 'Who goes there?' But the figure walked through the musket, upon which he dropped it and ran for the guardhouse. The next sentry saw all this take place and fired off his gun to alarm the guard. The figure then glided past a third sentry who was placed near the ruins of Pater old Church, and who watched her, or it, mount the top of a grave in the old churchyard, point with her finger to Heaven, and then stand till she vanished from his sight.

The sergeant of the guard came with rank and file to learn the tale, and the fright of the sentries all along the Dockyard wall was so great that none would remain at their posts unless they were doubled, which they were, as may be seen by the 'Report of the guard' for that night.*

Singularly enough, since then, the ghost has never been heard of again on board the *Asp*, and I never again heard the noises which before had so incessantly annoyed me.

The only clue I could ever find to account for my vessel being haunted is as follows: Some years previously to my having her, the *Asp* had been engaged as a mail packet between Port Patrick and Donaghadee. After one of her trips, the passengers having all disembarked, the stewardess, on going into the ladies' cabin, found a beautiful girl with her throat cut lying on one of the berths quite dead! How she came by her death no one could tell, and though, of course, strict investigations were commenced, neither who she was nor where she came from or anything about her was ever discovered.

The circumstances gave rise to much talk, and the vessel was remanded by the authorities, and she was

* It is interesting to compare this with the experiences of the guards in the Tower of London, which I describe in *Haunted Houses* (Piccolo). A. C.

not again used until handed over to me for surveying service. Here ends my tale, which I have given in all truth. Much as I know one gets laughed at for believing in ghost stories you are welcome to make what you please with this true account of the apparition on board the *Asp*.

CHAPTER TEN

A Spectral Wedding Party

From time to time in the grounds of Featherstone Castle, near Haltwhistle, Northumberland, the ghostly members of a wedding party can be seen by those who have the gift. How it came about that a bride, her groom and their guests haunt the castle is one of Northumberland's most famous legends.

Abigail Featherstonhaugh was a very beautiful young woman, the daughter of a powerful baron. Her good looks and her father's money and influence could have won for her any man in the land. As it was, she fell in love with a boy who was as poverty-stricken as he was handsome. Her father, of course, would not hear of their marrying; the fellow was not at all good enough for his daughter. So the baron himself selected a husband, a man of suitably high station and sufficient wealth. Unfortunately, he was possessed of very little else to commend him: his temper was dull, his physique poor and his features plain. At the same time as this marriage of convenience was foisted on a distressed Abigail her true love was banished from the castle and all the district under the baron's rule for the rest of his life. Then, against the abject pleas and constant objections of the poor bride, the wedding took place as planned in detail by the baron himself.

As soon as the ceremony was over, the marriage party, including the bride and her maids, the unwillingly accepted groom and his numerous friends, set off on horseback to ride round the estate before returning to the castle where the baron had arranged an enormous banquet in celebration of the union.

But evening came, and the party had not returned. In the castle all was ready: the food, the servants to serve it, the minstrels with their music rehearsed, and, in the kitchen, the cooks and their skivvies growing more vexed by the minute as they watched their carefully prepared dishes of food spoiling. The baron himself paced the hall, first in annoyance, and then, as the evening turned to night, in anxiety for the safety of his daughter. Finally, he sent out messengers to scour the land for the lost couple and their friends.

It was dawn before a cry went up: 'They're come at

last!' Sure enough, the tramp of horses' hooves was heard, and the party came in sight. Bride and groom and following attendants crossed the moat, passed under the gateway, dismounted, and entered the hall through the great door at its further end. First came the bridegroom, then the bride, and then followed the rest, taking their seats on each side. But during all this time not a word was spoken. The silence was heavy on them all. And when the baron and the waiting servants looked into their faces they saw with horror that fresh blood streamed down the cheeks of each one.

The baron fainted. The servants stood fixed in their places, unable to take their appalled eyes from the ghastly sight. At this moment a strong, rushing wind swirled through the hall, and when the baron and his servants came to their shocked senses, the ghostly wedding party had vanished.

A search was at once organized. And in a secluded dell called Pinkingscleugh Glen the bodies of the bride, her husband and their friends were found terribly slaughtered. Who the murderers were no one ever discovered for certain. But many believed that Abigail's true love, maddened by his unrequited passion, rounded up some accomplices, ambushed the unfortunate party, and took a vicious vengeance. Some say that afterwards he killed himself too. And so it is that according to the legend:

Still from the rocks at Pinkyncleugh
The blood of the murdered flows anew;

And that of the murderer drops alone
Into the pool 'neath the Raven's stone.

So it is, too, that those who have the eye for apparitions see, on the anniversary of the fatal wedding day each year, the bridal group progressing in ghostly form into the old tower at Featherstone.

CHAPTER ELEVEN

Dancing with the Dead

There is a kind of ghost which psychical researchers call 'crisis ghosts'. They are the apparitions of people on the point of death, or undergoing some intense experience in their lives. And the apparitions are seen by relatives or friends some distance away, who have no idea what is happening. There are many cases recorded in the annals of the Society for Psychical Research, but one which amuses as well as interests me was recounted by Lord Brougham in his auto-biography published in 1871. Here is his story:

A most remarkable thing happened to me, so

remarkable that I must tell the story from the beginning. After I left the High School [in Edinburgh], I went with G—' my most intimate friend, to attend the classes in the University. There was no divinity class, but we frequently in our walks discussed and speculated upon many grave subjects, among others, on the immortality of the soul, and on a future state. This question and the possibility, I will not say of ghosts walking, but of the dead appearing to the living, were subjects of much speculation; and we actually committed the folly of drawing up an agreement, written with our blood, to the effect that whichever of us died first should appear to the other, and thus solve any doubts we had entertained of the 'Life after Death'.

After we had finished classes at the College, G— went to India, having got an appointment there in the Civil Service. He seldom wrote to me, and after the lapse of a few years, I had almost forgotten him; moreover, his family having little connection with Edinburgh, I seldom saw or heard anything of them, or of him through them, so that all the old schoolboy intimacy had died out, and I had nearly forgotten his existence.

One evening I had taken a warm bath, and while in it and enjoying the comfort of the heat after the freezing I had undergone, I turned my head towards the chair on which I had deposited my clothes, as I was about to get out of the bath. On the chair sat G—, looking calmly at me. How I got out of the bath I know not, but on recovering my senses I found myself sprawling on the floor. The apparition, or whatever it was that had taken the likeness of G——, had disappeared. The vision produced such a shock, that I had no inclination to talk about it, or to speak about it . . . but the impression it made upon me was too vivid to be easily forgotten; and so strongly was I affected by it, that I have here written down the whole history with the date 19 December, and all the particulars as they are now fresh before me.

This is the account as Lord Brougham described it in a note he wrote immediately after the event in 1799. When writing his autobiography many years later, in October 1862, he copied out the note and added this:

. . . And now to finish the story begun about sixty years since. Soon after my return to Edinburgh, there arrived a letter from India, announcing G——'s death! and stating that he had died on the 19 December.

An even more eerie crisis ghost was recorded by Augustus Hare, an enthusiastic collector of such stories, in his book *In My Solitary Life*:

Two beautiful but penniless sisters were taken out in London by an aunt. A young gentleman from the North, of very good family and fortune, fell in love with one of them, and proposed to her, but she was with difficulty persuaded to accept him, and afterwards could never be induced to fix a date for their marriage. The young man, who was very much in love, urged and urged, but on one excuse or another, he was always put off. Whilst things were in this unsettled state, the young woman was invited to a ball. Her lover implored her not to go to it, and when she insisted, he made her promise not to dance any round of dances, saying that if she did, he should believe she had ceased to care for him.

The young lady went to the ball, and, as usual, all the young men gathered round her, trying to persuade her to dance. She refused any but square dances. At last, however, as a delightful waltz was being played, and she standing looking longingly on, she suddenly felt herself seized round the waist, and hurried into the dance. Not till she reached the end of the room, very angry, did she succeed in seeing with whom she had been forced to dance: it was her own betrothed.

Furious, she said she would never forgive him. But, as she spoke, he disappeared. She begged several young men to look for him, but he could not be found anywhere, and, to her astonishment, everyone denied having seen him. On reaching home, she found a telegram telling her of his death, and when the hours were compared, he was found to have died at the very moment when he had seized her for the dance.

Mrs Thompson Hankey [from whom Mr Hare heard the story] knew all the persons concerned.

CHAPTER TWELVE

Ghosts at War

In war, men, women and children die ugly, unnecessary deaths. So it is not surprising that many stories are told about ghosts being seen at battlefields, and about apparitions of slain people appearing before their horrified relatives and friends. During the First World War thousands of such visions were reported. Cases like this one, told by the sister of a soldier who was dying at about the time she saw his ghost:

I was awakened one night by three figures entering the bedroom; one in white between two soldiers in khaki.

I drew my husband's attention to it, but he could not see anything and said: 'Now, it's just fancy; try and get to sleep.' I was just going over when they entered for the second time. I shall never forget it, for I knew there must be something coming concerning my much-loved brother. Three weeks later I had a letter from his officer saying my brother had been killed on the night of my vision.

Soldiers engaged in a battle have often seen apparitions. A non-commissioned officer recorded his experience at such a time:

I was with my battalion in the retreat from Mons on or about 28 August 1914. The weather was very hot and clear, and between eight and nine in the evening, I was standing with a party of nine other men on duty, and some distance on either side there were parties of ten on guard. Immediately behind us, half of my battalion was on the edge of a wood, resting. An officer suddenly came up to us in a state of great anxiety and asked if we had seen anything startling. He hurried away from my tent to the next party of ten. When he had got out of sight, I, who was in charge, ordered two men to go forward out of the way of the trees in order to find out what the officer meant.

The two men returned saying they could see no sign of any Germans; at that time we thought that the officer must be expecting a surprise attack.

Immediately afterwards, the officer came back and

taking me and some others a few yards away, told us to look at the sky.

I could see quite plainly in mid-air, a strange light which seemed to be quite distinctly outlined and was not a reflection of the moon, nor were there any clouds in the neighbourhood.

The light became brighter and I could see quite distinctly three shapes, one in the centre having what looked like outspread wings, the other two were not so large, but were quite plainly distinct from the centre one.

They appeared to have a long, loose hanging garment of a golden tint and they were above the German line facing us.

We stood watching them for about three-quarters of an hour. All the men with me saw them, and other men came up from the groups who also told us they had seen the same thing.

I remember the day, because it was a day of terrible anxiety for us. The Uhlans had attacked us and we drove them back with heavy loss. It was after this engagement, when we were dog-tired, that the vision appeared.

Other soldiers described this vision, too. One man claimed that the figures 'kept growing brighter and brighter. The faces could be described, but you couldn't see what they were like. Under the feet of the three figures was a bright star and when the figures disappeared, the star remained.'

What was it these soldiers saw? Were there in fact heavenly bodies floating about in the sky? Or were the men so exhausted after their devastating battle that their weary minds played tricks on them? No one can answer these questions for certain. But one thing is sure: the soldiers experienced *something*. Exactly what and whether or not they were seeing ghosts or suffering from hallucinations must remain a mystery until psychical research improves our knowledge of such strange events. Meanwhile we can only wonder at and puzzle over the extraordinary things witnessed during wartime. A lieutenant-colonel, for example, recorded this story:

On the night of 27 August 1914, I was riding along in the column with two other officers. We had been talking and doing our best to keep from falling asleep on our horses.

As we rode along, I became conscious of the fact that in the fields on both sides of the road, I could see a very large body of horsemen. These horsemen had the appearance of squadrons of cavalry and they seemed to be riding across the fields, going in the same direction as we were going and keeping level with us. The night was not very dark. I did not say a word about it at first but I watched them for twenty minutes. The two other officers had stopped talking. At last one of them asked me if I saw anything in the fields. I then told him what I had seen. The third officer confessed that he too had been watching these horsemen for the past twenty minutes.

So convinced were we that they were really cavalry, that at the next halt one of the officers took a party of men out to reconnoitre but found no one there.

The night then grew darker and we saw no more.

Of course, we were all dog-tired and over-taxed, but it is an extraordinary thing that the phenomenon should have been witnessed by so many different people.

So far all these ghosts were ones people encountered while war was being fought. But there is another kind of war-ghost. These are apparitions of people who took part in battles waged long ago. J. R. W. Coxhead told the story of one of these ghosts in his book *Devon Traditions and Folklore*:

On a fine, sunny afternoon in the year 1904 a party of small children, led by a schoolmistress, were going for a walk up Marlpit's Hill to the south of the little market town of Honiton. They had just passed the bend in the road by the beautiful fifteenth-century Church of St Michael, and were nearing the little thatched cottage which used to stand on a narrow strip of ground on the right-hand side of the road, when suddenly the children noticed a strange-looking man coming down the hill towards them.

The man was exceptionally tall, and very wild of aspect. He was wearing a black, broad-brimmed hat, and a long brown coat, and he was staring straight in front of him in rather a dazed kind of way. His queer, old-fashioned clothes were tattered and torn, and much bespattered with mud.

As he passed by, the children stared at him with their eyes filled with apprehension. The school-mistress, noticing the children's frightened glances, said in a surprised voice, 'What on earth are you all looking at?'

One of the children whispered nervously, 'We are looking at that funny man.'

'What silly nonsense!' said the mistress. 'I can't see any funny man. There is nobody on the road except ourselves.'

The children were so insistent about the fact that they had seen the man, and were able to describe his dress and wild appearance so clearly that the school-mistress mentioned the peculiar incident to Miss Barnett, the Headmistress, when she returned to the school on Church Hill after the walk.

On further inquiries being made, it was discovered that a man who was living in the cottage in 1685 took part in Monmouth's Rebellion, and fought at the Battle of Sedgemoor. When the ill-fated Duke's army was defeated, the man managed to escape from the dreadful scene of carnage that followed, and, by hiding during the day in muddy ditches and travelling furtively by night, he eventually succeeded in reaching his cottage on the slopes of Marlpit's Hill.

Just as his wife and children were running from the

cottage to greet the exhausted fugitive, a party of troopers from the Royal army galloped up and cut him to pieces with their cavalry swords, in full view of his horror-stricken wife and family . . .

A man living not far from the village of Offwell, near Honiton, told the author of this book that his father saw the ghost in 1907. He was walking up Marlpit's Hill one night when the full moon was riding high in the sky. It was almost as light as day, and suddenly the apparition appeared in the road ahead of him. He was terribly frightened, but before the thing vanished he noticed that it was very tall and wore a black wide-brimmed hat.

That certainly is a convincing tale. But the most famous of all such 'after battle' hauntings takes place at Edge Hill in Warwickshire, scene of a fierce Civil War clash of arms. There, on Sunday, 23 October 1642, the Royalist troops of Charles I met Oliver Cromwell's Parliamentary army. Forty thousand men were locked in deadly and bitter combat. At the end neither side knew which had won, and Edge Hill was littered with the maimed and the dead. In the days that followed this blood-letting, rumours spread that the grisly battle was re-enacted on certain nights by ghostly soldiers. So disturbing were these stories that the King himself sent a team of officers to investigate. Colonel Lewis Kirke, Captain Dudley, Captain Wainman and three other trustworthy gentlemen looked into the affair and submitted a fascinating report of which the following is part, given in their own language, old-fashioned now but still vivid:

Edge Hill, in the very confines of Warwickshire, near unto Keynton, in Northamptonshire, a place, as appears by the sequel, destined for civil wars and battles; as where King John fought a battle with his barons, and where, in defence of the kingdom's laws and liberty, was fought a bloody conflict between His Majesty's and the Parliament's forces. At this Edge Hill, at the very place where the battle was fought, have since, and doth appear, strange and portentous apparitions of two jarring and contrary armies, as I shall in order deliver, it being certified by men of most credit in those parts, as William Wood, Esquire, Samuel Marshall, Minister, and others, on Saturday, which was in Christmas time . . . Between twelve and one o'clock in the morning was heard by some shepherds, and other countrymen, and travellers, first the sound of drums far off, and the noise of soldiers, as it were, giving out their last groans; at which they were much amazed, and stood still, till it seemed, by the nearness of the noise, to approach them; at which, too much affrighted, they sought to withdraw as fast as they possibly could; but then, on the sudden, whilst they were in their cogitations, appeared in the air the same incorporeal soldiers that made those clamours, and immediately, with ensigns displayed, drums beating, muskets going off, cannons discharged, horses neighing, which also to these men were visible, the alarum or entrance to this game of death was, one army, which gave the first charge, having the King's colours, and the other the Parliament's, at their head or front of the battle, and so pell-mell to it they went. The King's forces seemed at first to have the best, but afterwards to be put into apparent rout. But till two or three in the morning in equal scale continued this dreadful fight, the clattering of arms, noise of cannons, cries of soldiers, so amazing and terrifying that poor men, they could not believe they were mortal, or give credit to their eyes and ears; run away they durst not, for fear of being made a prey to these infernal soldiers, and so they, with much fear and affright, stayed to behold the success of the business, which at last suited to this effect. After some hours' fight, that army which carried the King's colours withdrew, or rather appeared to fly; the other remaining, as it were, masters of the field, stayed a good space triumphing, and expressing all the signs of joy and conquest, and then, with all their drums, trumpets, ordnance, and soldiers, vanished.

The poor men, glad that they were gone that had so long stayed them there against their wills, made with all haste to Keynton, and there knocking up Mr Wood, a Justice of the Peace, who called up his neighbour, Mr Marshall, the Minister, they gave them an account of the whole passage, and averred it upon their oaths to be true. At which affirmation of theirs, being much amazed, they should hardly have given credit to it, but would have conjectured the men to have been either

mad or drunk, had they not known some of them to
have been of approved integrity; and so, suspending
their judgements till the next night about the same
hour, they, with the same men, and all the substantial
inhabitants of that and the neighbouring parishes
drew thither; where, about half an hour after their
arrival, on Sunday, being Christmas night, appeared
in the same tumultuous warlike manner, the same two
adverse armies, fighting with as much spite and spleen
as formerly; and so departed the gentlemen and all the
spectators, much terrified with these visions of horror,
withdrawing themselves to their houses, beseeching
God to defend them from those hellish and prodigious
enemies. The next night they appeared not, nor all
that week, so that the dwellers thereabout were in good
hope they had for ever departed. But on the ensuing
Saturday night, in the same place, and at the same
hour, they were again seen with far greater tumult,
fighting in the manner aforementioned, for four hours,
or very near, and then vanished. Appearing again on
Sunday night, and performing the same actions of
hostility and bloodshed, so that Mr Wood and others,
whose faith, it should seem, was not strong enough to
carry them out against these delusions, forsook their
habitations thereabout, and retired themselves to
other more secure dwellings; but Mr Marshall stayed,
and some other; and so successively the next Saturday
and Sunday the same tumults and prodigious sights
and actions were put in the state and condition they
were formerly.

Not half so well known as the Edge Hill haunting but to my mind equally interesting is a similar kind of experience witnessed by two Scotsmen a hundred years or so after the English Civil War. The exact date is uncertain, and the author of the account unnamed, as are his father and grandfather who saw the apparition. Nevertheless, setting the story against other well attested hauntings, it does have a convincing ring of truth about it and serves to round off this chapter of wartime spectres:

As you wish to have an account of the vision which my father and grandfather saw in the neighbourhood of this place [Inverary], I will endeavour to comply with your request. I have heard it, with all its circumstances, so often related by them both, when together, as well as by my father separately, since my grandfather's decease, that I am as fully convinced that they saw this vision, as if I had seen it myself. At the same time I must acknowledge that, however desirous I am to oblige Lady — and you, I commit this account to writing with some degree of reluctance, well-knowing how little credit is generally given, by the more intelligent classes of mankind, to a narrative of that kind, and how little corresponds with the ordinary course of causes and events.

This vision was seen by them about three o'clock in the afternoon of a very warm, clear sunshiny day, in the month of June or July, between the years 1746 and 1753. I cannot go nearer to ascertain the year.

My grandfather was then a farmer in Glenary (which you know is within four miles of this place), and my father, who was at that time a young unmarried man, resided in the family with him.

On the morning of the day above-mentioned, my grandfather having occasion to transact some business in Glenshiray, took my father along with him. They went there by crossing the hill which separates it from Glenary; and their business in Glenshiray having been finished a little after midday, they came round by Inverary, in order to return home.

As soon as they came to Gairan Bridge, and had turned towards Inverary, they were very much surprised to behold a great number of men under arms, marching on foot towards them. At this time the foremost ranks were only advanced as far as Kilmalien. They were marching in regular order, and as closely as they could move, from that point of the new town near the Quay, where Captain Gillie's house now stands, along the shore and high road, and crossing the River Avay near the town, at or about the spot where the new bridge has been since built; of the rear there appeared to be no end. The ground upon which the town now stands was then surrounded by a park wall. From the nature of the ground my father and grandfather could see no further than this wall; and as the army was advancing in front, the rear as regularly succeeded, and advanced from the furthest verge of their view.

They stood a considerable time to observe this extraordinary sight, then walked slowly on, but stopped now and then, with their eyes constantly fixed on the objects before them. Meantime, the army continuing regularly to advance, they counted that it had fifteen or sixteen pairs of colours; and they observed that the men nearest to them were marching upon the road, six or seven abreast, or in each line, attended by a number of women and children, both below and above the road, some of whom were carrying tin cans and other implements of cookery, which, I am told, is customary on the march. They were clothed in red (but as to that particular circumstance I do not recollect whether my grandfather mentioned it or not, though I know my father did), and the sun shone so bright that the gleam of their arms, which consisted of muskets and bayonets, sometimes dazzled their sight. They also observed between Kilmalien and the Salmon Draught, an animal resembling a deer or a horse, in the middle of a crowd of soldiers, who were, as they conjectured, stabbing and pushing it forward with their bayonets.

My father, who had never seen an army before, naturally put a number of questions to my grandfather (who had served in the Argyll Highlanders in assisting to suppress the rebellion of 1745) concerning the probable route and destination of the army which was now advancing towards them, and of the number of men it seemed to consist of. My grandfather replied that he supposed it had come from Ireland, and had landed at Kyntyre, and that it was proceeding to England; and that, in his opinion, it was more numerous than the army on both sides at the battle of Culloden. My father having particularly remarked that the rear ranks were continually coming forward in order to overtake those who were before them, and inquiring the reason, my grandfather told him that this was always the case with the rear; that the least obstacle stopped and threw them behind, which necessarily, and in a still greater degree, retarded the march of those who were behind them, and obliged them to come forward until they recovered their own places again. And he therefore advised my father, if he went into the army, to endeavour, if possible, to get into the front rank, which always marched with leisure and ease, while those in the rear were generally kept running in the manner he had seen.

My father and grandfather were now come to the Thorn Bush between the Gairan Bridge and the gate of the Deer Park, and at the same time the rear of the army had advanced very near the gate. And as the road forms a right angle at that gate, and the front of the army was then directly opposite them, they had, of course, a better opportunity of observing it minutely. The vanguard, they then observed, consisted of a party of forty or fifty men, preceded by an officer on foot. At a little distance behind them another officer appeared, riding upon a grey dragoon-horse. He was the only person they observed on horseback, and from his appearance and station in the march they considered him as the commander-in-chief. He had on a gold-laced hat, and a blue hussar-cloak, with wide, open, loose sleeves, all lined with red. He also wore boots and spurs; the rest of his dress they could not see. My father took such particular notice of him, that he often declared he would know him perfectly well if he ever saw him again. Behind this officer the rear of the army marched all in one body, so far as they observed, but attended by women and children, as I mentioned above.

My father's curiosity being now sufficiently gratified, he represented to my grandfather that these men, who were advancing towards them, would force them to go along with them, or use them otherwise ill; and he therefore proposed that they should both go out of their way by climbing over a stone dyke which fences the Deer Park from the high road. To this my grandfather objected, saying that as he was a middle-aged man, and had seen some service, he believed they would not give any trouble to him, but at the same time he told my father, that as he was a young man, and they might possibly take him along with them, he might go out of the way or not, as he thought fit. Upon this my father instantly leaped over the dyke. He then walked behind it for a little time; but when he arrived near the clumps, he looked back to observe the motions of the army, and found, to his utter astonishment, that they were all vanished, not a soul of them was to be seen.

As soon as he had recovered from his surprise, he returned to my grandfather, and cried out, 'What has

become of the men?' My grandfather, who did not
seem to have paid them much attention after my father
left him, then observed also that they had disappeared,
and answered back with an equal degree of astonishment, 'that he could not tell'.

As they proceeded on their way to Inverary, he
recommended my father to keep what he had seen
secret, lest they should make themselves ridiculous, for
that no person would believe they had seen a vision
so extraordinary; at the same time he told him that
though he (my grandfather) might not live to see it,
my father might possibly live to see the vision realized.

This conversation was scarcely ended, when they
met one Stewart, an old man who then resided in
Glenshiray, going home, and driving a horse before
him. This, as they believed, was the same animal they
had before observed surrounded by a crowd. My father,
notwithstanding the admonition he had just received,
asked Stewart what had become of the people who
were travelling with him. Stewart, not understanding
the drift of the question, answered that nobody had
been in company with him since he left Inverary,
but that he never travelled in so warm a day, that the
air was so close and sultry that he was scarcely able
to breathe, and that his horse had become so weak and
feeble, that he was obliged to alight and drive it before
him.

The account of this vision was communicated by my
father and grandfather, not only to me, but to many
others in this place and neighbourhood, it being

scarcely possible that so extraordinary an occurrence could long be concealed. It is no doubt extremely difficult to account for it, but no person acquainted with my father or grandfather ever supposed that either of them was capable of inventing such a story; and accordingly, as far as I can understand, no person to whom they told it ever doubted that they told the truth. My grandfather died several years ago; my father died within these two years; but neither of them saw their vision realized, although, indeed, my father had strong expectations of seeing it realized a few years before his death, particularly at the time of the Irish rebellion, and of the last threatened invasion of the French.

CHAPTER THIRTEEN

The Sailor-Ghosts at the Punch Bowl

In the early days of 1973 the inhabitants of Sefton, in Lancashire, were arguing about some strange goings-on which were disturbing the peace of their ancient village. Until then Sefton had been visited mostly by people interested in the beautiful, carved wooden stalls and pulpit, and the remarkable brass monuments to the Molyneaux family, that adorn the fourteenth-century church. Now there was something other than ecclesiastical furnishings to be looked at, something far less solid and tangible, but, people said, something almost as old.

Just across the churchyard from the church stands

the Punch Bowl Inn, once the vicarage, now a popular, well-run public house. It was here on New Year's Eve 1972 that Mrs Peggy Wilding, a member of the inn's staff, saw the figure of a young man, his head shrouded in what looked like mist, floating along the upstairs landing. Shaken, as well she might be, by such an unexpected vision, Mrs Wilding fled downstairs and told the rest of the staff what she had witnessed. Puzzled, curious, a little scared, they all trooped upstairs to look at the young chap for themselves. He was, of course, nowhere to be found.

'At first I thought that the ghost was just my own reflection in a window,' Mrs Wilding told the *Crosby Herald*, whose reporter published the story on 2 February 1973, 'but I realized that it could not have been, for its face was that of a young man. You can imagine how scared I was.'

Mrs Wilding was not alone for long, either in seeing the ghost or being frightened by it. A waitress colleague walked into the bar called the News Room at the back of the inn one day and saw a man dressed in sailor's uniform sitting in a corner by the fireplace. Men wearing sailor's clothes or any other form of dress are not exactly an unusual sight in a public house, so something about the figure must have startled the waitress. Whatever it was, she screamed and ran out of the room. When she calmed down and plucked up her courage to go back into the bar, the sailor was gone.

He could, of course, have been an entirely ordinary,

flesh-and-blood customer who had not been too pleased to be screamed at, and left, disgruntled with this nervous kind of service. The waitress, having heard Mrs Wilding's story, might easily have been jumpy – fearful of meeting a ghost herself. She did not think so, however. What is more, other people began to talk about a sailor they had seen in the News Room. And others claimed they saw doors open by themselves, and heard footsteps at night for which there seemed to be no cause.

A barmaid was the first to be attacked by a spirit. She was, she said, pushed down the stairs by a ghostly figure. Outside in the car park, a regular customer was gripped by invisible hands and thrown from his bicycle. 'I did not fall,' he told the *Crosby Herald* reporter, 'I was physically dragged off it, by something or someone that I could not see.'

Very soon it came to light that these 1973 hauntings were not the first in the area. Another of the pub's regulars was sitting in the bar one afternoon some time before when someone came in saying that a man dressed like an old-fashioned mariner was digging up a grave in the churchyard. When they went to find out who the man was, he had gone; but a fresh pile of earth lay on an unmarked grave.

A young man on the upstairs landing, a spectral figure that attacks a waitress, a sailor in the bar and another (or the same one?) in the churchyard: were all these imagined or was there something ghostly really going on at Sefton? Even the villagers disagreed about the answers. But certainly the Punch Bowl has the kind of history you would expect of a haunted house. Five hundred years or so ago the sea reached almost to the Punch Bowl's doors. In those days the house was the church vicarage, and whenever a ship was wrecked off shore, drowned sailors used to be washed up nearby. Sefton folk used to bring their bodies to the vicarage where they were laid out in the back room – the same room that is now the News Room bar. Later they were buried in the churchyard, their graves left unmarked if their identities were unknown.

Might this explain why spectral figures haunt the pub? Or is it all local gossip and shadows in the night seen by the half-drunk eyes of some of the Punch Bowl's customers? Perhaps no one will ever know for certain. But Mrs Wilding and her colleagues are less sceptical. For them the Punch Bowl's ghosts are real enough to be frightening.

CHAPTER FOURTEEN

The Old Ghost-Layer

Ask the question, 'What would you do if you found a ghost haunting your house?' and most people will answer, 'Try to get rid of it.' There are all kinds of ways used to lay ghosts – 'exorcize' them is the technical word. But every method includes the saying of prayers or the casting of spells, and the performance of ritual acts. The Roman Catholic Church and the Church of England, for example, have special services used in exorcisms. Mediums in the Spiritualist movement sometimes try to speak to the ghost, asking why it is haunting the place and how it can be made peaceful. Witches and warlocks, in the days when they were listened to more than they are now, used charms and ancient spells to conjure up and then banish apparitions. And even quite recently wise old women would sometimes be asked to rid a house of a bothersome spirit.

A story about one such old sybil was told by Myra E. Jennings in the summer 1934 number of the magazine *Old Cornwall*. She had heard the tale from her mother, who in turn had heard it from her grandmother. So the story must have happened some time earlier than 1820 or thereabouts.

A wayside cottage had belonged to two old people, who died, leaving it in very bad repair. Their only son had gone out years before to Australia, and no word had been heard from him since. So, after some time the cottage was done up, and new tenants moved in.

They found it impossible to live there, though, because of the strange sounds they heard at night. So badly was the cottage haunted that, though the parson was called in, his efforts were all in vain, and it remained empty.

Then, one day, an old stranger woman came through the village, selling brooms, and, hearing of the haunted house, she offered to lay the spirit herself. All she asked for was a fire in the room, a table and chair, a Bible, and some sewing to busy her hands with.

These she was gladly given, and she settled down to keep her lonely watch.

At midnight, the door burst open, and in lurched – a monstrous pig! Laying her hand on the Holy Book, the old woman said, 'Satan, depart, and let this spirit come back in its natural form!' At this, the pig went out, and a young man came in its place, and when told to 'speak, in God's name!' this is the story he told:

He was the missing son of the old people who had lived there. Out in Australia he had fallen on bad times, and for lack of any good news to send had not written home for years. Suddenly he struck gold, and having made his fortune, he decided to come home and give his parents a joyful surprise. He arrived at the town near his old home too late to bank his money as he intended, and took it with him, as he walked out to his parents' cottage. When he got there and found that he had altered so much that his own parents did not recognize him, he carried on the joke, as he thought, by asking and obtaining a night's lodging; and, listening over a scanty supper to their tale of poverty and distress, he went to bed glad in his heart to think of the grand sensation he would cause when he revealed himself and his riches in the morning.

But the old people, poor wretches, were even more desperate than he realized. Somehow they had caught the gleam or felt the weight of his gold, and, falling under the dreadful temptation, they killed the 'stranger' in his sleep, and buried him behind the house.

'Come,' said the spirit, 'and see where my bones lie. Let them be gathered, and laid in consecrated ground, and I will trouble this place no more.'

The old woman followed, and, as the spirit hovered over one particular spot in the garden, and then disappeared, fearing that she should not recognize the exact spot by daylight, she took off the thimble which she was still wearing, and with it marked the place. Next day, the ground was dug over, bones were found there, and duly buried in the churchyard, after which the cottage remained as quiet at night as any other.

CHAPTER FIFTEEN

The Haunted Bowling Alley

Just as I was finishing this book, I received a letter from Mr W. V. Cleveley, who was living in Germany for a while, and had read the stories in *More Haunted Houses*. He wrote to tell me about a strange experience he had had, and his account is so interesting that I include it here just as he told it.

I am thirty-one years of age and having left school at fifteen I joined Rank Organization cinemas, and after six years, joined their Bowling Divison. I was employed as a mechanic at the new Bowl in Brook Street in Chester. Before being a bowling centre the building had been the Gaumont Cinema.

When I started work there my boss was Mr Fred Dickenson, who had been chief projectionist at the Gaumont. We were talking together one day and I was told by Mr Dickenson about the resident ghost, whose name was George.

I have an open mind about such matters and I must admit I took what he told me with a large pinch of salt. He said that during the war he heard a noise on the projection box roof. There was one loud thud followed by two small thuds. At the time an air raid was in progress and Mr Dickenson and his assistant thought a German pilot had baled out and landed on the roof. The thuds sounded like a body dropping followed immediately by the legs hitting the roof. The roof was searched but nothing was found. This happened many times again, always during an air raid, and always nothing was found.

Again in the same projection box there were three rooms (see drawing, fig 1). Mr Dickenson was running the show, in the main box; his assistant was in the rewinding room, spooling film. Mr Dickenson turned from the projector and looked towards a small window. In this window he saw the face of a man looking at him. He assured me that it was not his reflection in the glass nor light from the projector playing tricks. Mr Dickenson moved into the room his assistant was in and told him that somebody was in the other small room and to go through his door into the same room.

It was impossible for anyone to be in the room and get out without passing either man; the only window opened to a drop of some eighty feet. When the two men entered the room it was empty.

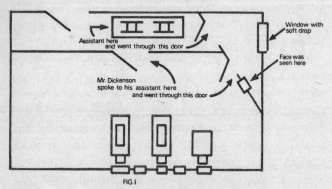

Window with soft drop

Assistant here and went through this door

Face was seen here

Mr. Dickenson spoke to his assistant here and went through this door

FIG. 1

Now, about my own experience of the same 'ghost'. My workmate and myself finished work at the Bowling Centre at approximately two AM, having seen the Midnight League finish their last game. Being the middle of winter and the roads being bad with ice and snow, I was unable to get home on my motor bike and often stayed in the Bowl workshop and got my head down on a couple of chairs. This night, the weather was really bad and my mate decided to stay also. The Bowl was empty but for the two of us. A check was always made each night for any strays who wanted a night out of the cold.

My workmate decided he would make a cup of coffee before turning in; meanwhile I had a wash. My mate was in the workshop and I was having my wash in the staff room, approximately fifteen yards from the workshop (see drawing, fig two). There was a crash, and I thought, 'There go the cups.' Ready to go up in the air with my mate, I ran onto the old stage of the cinema, which after redevelopment had been left as no use could be made of it. On the stage I met my workmate who was on his way to see what I had dropped. We laughed and said it must have been George, and went back to what we had left. Within seconds of getting back to the washroom, I heard another crash coming from the direction of the stage. I arrived back on the stage to meet my friend coming from the workshop. He had heard the second crash and came to look at what had happened. As the stage was not in use any more the only lights were four sixty-watt lamps, just enough light to see your way across to the bowling machines. In the centre of the stage we found a sheet of broken glass. On seeing this we thought it had fallen from the windows in the scenery flies which were almost one hundred feet above us. We looked up and in between the strips of wood that the men working on the scenery walked on, we could see something or someone moving across the flies. Thinking that someone might have broken in and managed to climb the single iron ladder to the top of the flies we called out to him, pointing out that he could slip through one of the pulley holes and fall the one hundred feet to the stage. The 'thing', whatever it was, took no notice of our warnings and continued to cross the floor of the flies from one side to the other.

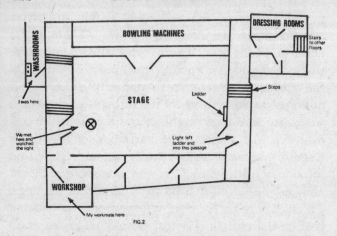

FIG. 2

A thought crossed my mate's mind and he said that the 'thing' could be caused by stray light from a passing car, reflecting off the canal outside and casting a shadow on the flies. We agreed on this and were just about to leave the stage when the light moved back across the flies towards the ladder. The iron ladder which was bolted to the wall ran from the stage to the top and anybody who had reason to climb this vertical ladder had a good climb in front of them. The light started to move slowly down the rungs of the ladder just as if someone was shining a torch on the ladder, and at this moment we realized that the light did not come from a car's headlights. It would be impossible for the reflection to shine at such an angle. Having reached the stage, the light passed through an open door and into a passage, and out of sight.

What we did next I cannot explain. My mate and

myself telephoned the police and within minutes a number of policemen from Chester station of the Cheshire Police had positioned themselves around the whole building. My workmate and myself were confronted by an inspector and a sergeant. When we had finished, the inspector told the sergeant to climb the ladder to the top and see if he could find anything. I don't know if the sergeant was afraid of heights or what, but he refused to climb the ladder. At this, the inspector radioed for a dog and handler, and they arrived and were told our story.

The inspector asked us to show him where the passage led that the light went into. This was also part of the old cinema and led to the dressing rooms in which the stars used to prepare themselves. These were no longer in use, and but for a few boxes, the rooms were empty.

Having passed through the passage we entered the small building by the only unlocked door. There were three rooms on the ground floor, three on the first floor, and one room built in the attic. As these rooms were not in use, there were no lights, so the police torches were the only illumination. The inspector told the dog handler to go in first with his dog. This he did with us all following behind. The dog led the way and sniffed around in all the rooms on the ground floor and first floor. But when he came to the attic he refused to pass through the door and even though the handler pulled on the lead the dog cried and cowered away, the fur on his back standing on end.

The inspector rushed into the small room followed by the sergeant but it was completely empty. The dog still refused to enter, however. Later the handler said he had not seen anything like it before.

That was the last time I saw anything in the Bowl even though I stayed there for another year.

This is the story as best I can remember it. I'm sure that a report was made to the Police HQ at Chester regarding that night. It happened in the winter of 1964.

The building is still standing, but is now a bingo hall. The stage is there but the dressing rooms have been knocked down for a road to pass near the building.

As I said at the beginning, I keep a very open mind, but this sticks in my memory and even nine years later I still wonder what it was that happened that night.

1 November 1973.   *W. V. Cleveley.*

Acknowledgements

'Uncle Bert Returns' is from *Apparitions and Haunted Houses* by Sir Ernest Bennett, published by Faber and Faber; the poem, 'The Little Blue Flame', is from *A Book of Folklore* by Sabine Baring-Gould, published by Collins; the Marlpit's Hill apparition (p 97) is from *Devon Traditions and Folklore* by J. R. W. Coxhead. Every effort has been made to contact copyright holders; the author will gladly make good in future editions any inadvertent omissions from these acknowledgements.

If you have enjoyed this PICCOLO Book you may like to choose your next book from the titles listed on the following pages.

Ghost Books

Also by Aidan Chambers

HAUNTED HOUSES (illus)   20p

True ghost stories of some of Britain's most celebrated haunted buildings, spine-chilling, hair-raising tales such as that of the drummer of Cortachy Castle, the ghostly skulls of Calgarth Hall, the Haunting of Epworth Parsonage and many others. A fascinating book not to be missed.

GREAT GHOSTS OF THE WORLD (illus)   25p

A fascinating collection of ghost stories such as the Indian Phantom, the Flying Dutchman, the stone-throwing ghost of Mauritius and stories of Vampires; they'll make you jump!

By Sorche Nic Leodhas
SCOTTISH GHOSTS (illus)   30p

This is a collection of ghost stories handed down from generation to generation by story-tellers now dead from the Highlands and Lowlands of Scotland. They'll make your blood run cold!

More Piccolo Fiction

Lavinia Derwent

SULA (illus)   25p

Magnus prefers animals to people. Living on
the remote Scottish island of Sula, he has
many friends, like 'Old Whiskers' the seal.
However, it takes the strange old hermit, Mr
Skinnymalink, to make him realize that perhaps people aren't so bad as he thought!

RETURN TO SULA (illus)   25p

More adventures of Magnus on the remote
Scottish island where he lives with his Gran.
He wins a drawing competition and has to go
to the mainland where he meets the Duke, as
wild and free as Magnus, and who knows a
vital secret about him . . .

Two fascinating and absorbing books not to
be missed!